# "You're the Only One Here Who Doesn't Look Like a Doctor"

*Portrait of a Woman Surgeon*

MARIE-CLAUDE WRENN

Thomas Y. Crowell Company
Established 1834 / New York

The quote on page 23 appeared in "Women Physicians: As Numbers Rise, So Does Status—Maybe," by Mary Lynn M. Luy, *Modern Medicine*, © 1975 by Harcourt Brace Jovanovich, Inc. The quote on page 28 is reprinted from "An Interview with Dr. Estelle Ramey," *Perspectives in Biology and Medicine,* Spring 1971, © 1971 by The University of Chicago. The quote on page 234 appeared in "The Psychodynamics of Power," *Mainliner* magazine, March 1977; reprinted courtesy of *Mainliner* magazine carried aboard United Airlines, © 1977 by East-/West Network, Inc.

Library of Congress Cataloging in Publication Data

Wrenn, Marie-Claude Palmieri.
   "You're the only one here who doesn't look like a doctor."
   1. Merrill, Alison. 2. Surgeons—Maryland—Biography. 3. Women surgeons—United States—Biography.
I. Title.
R154.M574W73    617'.092'4 [B]    77-7871
ISBN 0-690-01420-1

77 78 79 80 81 10 9 8 7 6 5 4 3 2 1

For reasons of privacy and patient confidentiality, all names in this book have been changed. Some ailments have been reworked in their medical details to further protect their source. All the events happened, and are described as they unfolded.

To
McDonald E.,
Edmund L.,
Edward and Edmund.
Their book too.

# Acknowledgments

Many people contributed so effectively to this book. I hope that the physicians who gave me generously of their time and who let me observe their work will be partially recompensed by taking pride in seeing their words on these pages. Others are not quoted here, but they helped, too. I am also grateful to the hospital staffs who let me come into their world to taste the day-to-day flavor of medicine. I am particularly grateful to the surgeon-heroine of this book, whose perceptiveness, common sense, and hard work impressed me from the start. My thanks to Philip Spitzer and to Cynthia Vartan, my editor, who helped with her sound suggestions about the manuscript. Dr. Michelle Warren, my sister, and her husband, Dr. Fiske Warren, were unfailingly patient in answering questions about the technicalities of what I had seen. I also appreciate the effort of friends who read and offered their sensitive suggestions. My special thanks to Jackie Dunko and Joyce McManus. I am very appreciative for the cooperation of Mary Ann Stewart director of the Tuxedo Park library. I owe a large debt of gratitude to my husband, who offered prickly criticisms about the manuscript and who, more than once, cared for our children in my absence. About the matter of child care he wryly said he did "Very well—for a man." To everyone who helped, many thanks. I couldn't have written this without them.

—MARIE-CLAUDE WRENN

# Contents

*"He tried to persuade me that in the responsible duties of relieving ills which flesh is heir to, it is appropriate that man be the physician, and woman the nurse. . . ."*
—*Dr. Elizabeth Blackwell,*
*the United States' first*
*woman physician, in 1846*

# "You're the Only One Here Who Doesn't Look Like a Doctor"

# Introduction

At different times during the feminist era, women left the Age of Victorian Womanhood for the Age of the Split-Level, for the Age of the Career. They are now seeking equality in combat, equality in the priesthood, and equal status on athletic fields. They are founding banks and joining police homicide squads. They aim for high-salaried corporate posts. Some are even practicing as intensely trained cardiovascular surgeons.

Who is she, this modern medical woman of the 1970s?

In the nineteenth century, women medical students were pelted with mud as well as insults as they walked in hooped petticoats to class. In Great Britain, a petition presented by a female Edinburgh 7 to sanction the admission of women into medical school was soundly rejected by parliamentary vote.

In 1847, when Elizabeth Blackwell knocked on the door of a little-known medical school, Geneva Medical College in Geneva, New York, the student body—mostly farm boys—roared with amusement, stomped their feet, and threw their hats in the air. She is largely credited with opening the medical profession to women in the United States, although the word "open" is historically debatable. More accurately, she set a first, important precedent by applying for and receiving a medical degree as a woman. Up to that time women had practiced medicine informally, mostly as midwives, learning the trade by apprenticeship.

Following an old tradition, some women managed to gain surreptitious admission to medical school by dressing as men. In ancient Greece, Agnodice, an Athenian midwife in the third century B.C., was brought to trial for such cleverness, since medical learning was forbidden to women and slaves. A surge of popular support from Agnodice's grateful female patients eventually left her free to practice her medical trade once again.

At autopsy in 1865, the British army was mortified to discover that its inspector-general and ranking medical officer was a she, not a he; Dr. James Barry, posthumously rumored to be the illegitimate daughter of a British lord, had managed both to obtain a Doctor of Medicine diploma from the University of Edinburgh and to safeguard her masquerade for more than fifty years.

Male disguise was precedent enough to be seriously suggested to Elizabeth Blackwell. She rightly felt that donning men's clothes would gain nothing for the future of professional womanhood. A strong-willed person, English-born Elizabeth Blackwell came from a nonconformist family, Dissenters to the established Church of England. Attracted to America as less traditional than European countries, the Blackwells eventually directed their nonconformity in religious matters to other areas, befriending Harriet Beecher Stowe and the antislavery movement and espousing a gamut of other liberal causes.

Elizabeth Blackwell's medical school graduation in 1849—or the backlash it engendered—spurred the founding of medical schools exclusively for women, none of which exist today in their original form. A few years later, when Blackwell's younger sister Emily (who is said to be the first American woman to have devoted a large part of her practice to surgery) applied to Geneva Medical College, she was refused. The administration, stung by censure from medical peers, remarked that "in no way had we intended to start a precedent."

When Elizabeth Blackwell tried to set up practice in New York City, no landlord would rent her space, no hospital would accept her on its staff. Her office practice was largely confined to Quakers, the advanced thinkers of their day. With the help of her Quaker friends, she eventually founded her own New York Infirmary for women and children, staffed by a nascent group of women doctors to cater to the health needs of New York City's immigrant hordes. A professional pariah herself, she ignored objections that the hospital would be used by "classes and persons whom it would be an insult to be called upon to deal with." Female doctors were too startling an innovation, Dr. Blackwell was told. They "would be looked upon with so much suspicion that the police would interfere."

Dr. Mary Edwards Walker, after serving three years as a volunteer nurse cum medical degree, eventually won a Civil War commission as a surgeon in the Union army, with the rank of first lieutenant. She became the only woman physician on active duty during the Civil War, the first Confederate woman prisoner of war, the first woman officer to be exchanged for a man of equal rank, and the only woman ever to win the Congressional Medal of Honor (1865). An early rebel against corsets and voluminous skirts, she wore her own version of a uniform on the battlefield and pantsuits during office hours, one hundred years before the latter fashion was reinvented by the Paris couturiers. Her Congressional Medal of Honor was rescinded in 1917 for insufficient evidence to support the award, fifty-two years after she achieved the right to wear the medal and three years before women won the right to vote. Her notoriety and unpopularity for her ardent support of the suffrage cause may have influenced the decision. But she refused to return the beribboned, star-shaped military medal awarded for bravery, and wore it proudly until her death.

In 1918, Dr. Alice Hamilton, whose founding work in the new field of industrial medicine had already led to the first workmen's compensation legislation for industrial diseases in the United States, was the first woman invited to join the Harvard Medical School faculty, a tradition-bound male bastion. A member of the board wanted reassurance that she would not insist on using the Harvard Club, which at that time did not even admit members' wives. One backer had to promise that she would not demand her quota of football tickets. Another vowed that she would not embarrass the rest of the faculty by marching in the commencement procession or sitting on the platform. A yearly commencement invitation carried this warning: "Under no circumstances may a woman sit on the platform."

A heavy overlay of Victorian prudery colored the nineteenth century's attitude toward its woman doctors. It was shocking for a woman to leave her home unchaperoned, much less to dissect a human body, or to see a naked man. It was even, at times, apparently unacceptable for a medical man to examine exposed female flesh. It is astounding to read in Dr. Samuel Gregory's *Letter to Ladies in Favor of Female Physicians* (Boston, 1854) that women in labor, finally faced with the facts of birthing, refused all medical help whatsoever rather than expose their genitalia to a member of the opposite sex. When Elizabeth Blackwell wrote a rather prudish book suggesting that women be given a minimum of physiological knowledge about their own bodies, eleven publishers refused her manuscript before she had it privately printed at her own expense.

Today, according to the latest American Medical Association statistics, there are only a dozen female urologists in the United States. One, a conservatively dressed thirty-eight-year-old woman who practices in Washington, D.C., says that her practice consists mostly of women and children, although women generally show little hesitation in seeking the services of a male obstetrician-gynecologist.

Now, 32,976 women in the United States are physicians—8.7 percent of the total number of physicians—according to the American Medical Association's *Physician Distribution and Medical Licensure in the U.S., 1975.* Women are not, however, distributed evenly throughout the profession. According to the A.M.A.'s *Special Tabulation, A.M.A. Physician Masterfile, 1975,* the greatest number, 23.4 percent, have chosen pediatrics; one of the smallest numbers, 3.1 percent, is found in general surgery. But the total number of women doctors is expected to increase. The percentage of women enrolled in medical schools rose from 9 percent during the 1969-70 school year to 22.4 percent in 1976-77. The periodical *Medical Economics,* in a cover story spotlighting a brazen clenched fist gripping an uplifted stethoscope, estimated that 50 percent of physicians in the United States will eventually be women.

"I was just so glad to be in medical school," says a woman surgeon who graduated from New York University Medical School in the 1940s, commenting on the attitude toward women in medical school during her student days. "They weren't taking as many men then because they might be drafted. So it was *easier* for a woman then, I'm sure. The women were so anxious to get through the first two years and not get flunked that I don't think they would have made a peep, even if they had felt strongly about something. We ladies automatically assumed that if we got in, we'd better hang in there and not make waves or they'd throw us out as troublemakers.

"Thinking back on it from this perspective of a raised consciousness, I think *I* was much more afraid of being thrown out than anything else. I mean, everybody had a level of anxiety. This used to be classic among all medical students. That anxiety was so classic that it's the only big thing I remember vividly from my years in medical school. We just figured that men were smarter, so we'd have to study harder.

"During the admissions interview I think they were probably trying to assess stability. I remember there used to be a rumor that if you bit your nails, you were *out.* I used to bite my nails. So I wore gloves through the whole interview, and a hat. No one ever went out into the street in those days without hats and gloves. Had they asked me why I had the gloves on, I was going to say 'A-lady-never-goes-anywhere-without-her-hat-and-gloves'—which is the way I was trained. So nobody was going to get those gloves off me come hell or high water."

Years ago, it was very difficult for a woman to obtain the necessary residency or training in general surgery. "I wanted to go into general surgery in 1950," a graying woman obstetrician-gynecologist told me. "But unless you had some real pull, there were no general residency programs in that field available to women."

"There's been some reluctance to take women into surgery," a nattily dressed male surgeon said to me, his hair modishly long with sideburns. He was enlightening me on the male mystique ingrained in surgery. "One, it's a tremendously demanding physical job even for the best male athlete. The second consideration is that there's a tremendous amount of time and money expended in training. There is the lingering fear that a woman will go out and get married and have children and never use this training. Today, if you're a girl, you don't have to get married; if you get married, you don't have to have children; and if you have children, you don't have to quit your job."

Says a university surgeon responsible for interviewing candidates for surgical residencies at his metropolitan hospital: "There's a silent quota. Nothing is ever said, but there's the underlying concern that if you take in too many women, they'll start taking over."

I myself grew up with an interest in medical women, starting with stories which filtered down from my father's sister, who attended Philadelphia's Women's Medical College in the thirties, at a time when few women applied and few were accepted. Changing with the times, this medical school is now coeducational and redubbed the Medical College of Pennsylvania. When my sister went through Cornell University's medical school in the sixties, I went to visit her there and at New York City's Bellevue Hospital during her internship, a period of her life when she barely had time to come home.

The story I tell here is the tale of one year in the life of a woman doctor, Alison Merrill, her first year as a young woman surgeon in the 1970s. With the permission of the hospitals involved, I followed her on her rotations through different hospital services, in and out of the operating rooms, wards, emergency rooms, and staff lounges, and partook of the leisure moments which were left. I interviewed other men and women, both physicians and patients, and their experiences contributed to the whole.

As she launches into her training, Alison faces one of the longest, most rigorous, and most difficult of all medical specialty trainings. Accepted into a good six-year program, later shortened to five, she begins as a junior assistant resident; as of July 1975, the traditional surgical internship year was absorbed into many residency training programs. Her tale is not written here as a universal or even feminist experience, but as a personal one, peculiar to her and to her times, in an age where women are breaking unknown professional ground, in a society which is still ambivalent toward the professional woman, in a field where women are yet a small minority.

# Part I

# MS. OR M.D.?

"There are three classes of human beings: men, women and women physicians."
—Sir William Osler, Professor of Medicine, the Johns Hopkins University School of Medicine, 1889—1904

# 1

# Ms. or M.D., a Small Snowball in Hell

"Let's not allow our love and respect for the ladies to blind us to the relative waste of giving them medical training."
—*Medical Economics*, December 4, 1961

I was a junior in high school, and I already knew that working in a hospital was more like medicine's answer to Dante's *Inferno* than Marcus Welby. TV medicine seems like a total fantasy to me now.

At the time I was sixteen, and a volunteer hospital candy-striper. I had joined the Girl Scout volunteer program at our small community hospital and wore a colorful red-and-white pinafore, bright and striped like a Christmas candy cane.

You could say that my medico-surgical career began with making patients' beds, washing dishes, pushing wheelchairs, feeding patients, distributing mail, and yes, even rinsing stainless-steel bedpans.

One of my more important jobs was to flush syringes and dulled needles clear of clotted blood with a soapy aseptic solution before they were sterilized. Our modest-sized hospital was still using reusable needles, which were a prime source of hepatitis. Thinking back, I'm not sure if our well-meaning but haphazard procedure wasn't helpful in spreading infection. I'm sorry to say that we occasionally dropped the needles on the floor and puzzled over which metal pans of equipment were or were not sterile.

It was during this time that I noticed all the little unsung, messy chores demanded of the nurses by the hospital doctors. For instance, the nursing staff had to suction out the respirator's endotracheal tube, an apparatus which is used to ventilate the lungs, helping a patient to breathe. If too much moisture collects at the bottom of the tube, which goes down the larynx and into the trachea, the patient may choke. It wasn't a glamorous job but a necessary one. Or if a drunk rolled in off the street—filthy, tattered, disoriented—the doctor on call would order a "STAT" (immediate) bath. Any bleeding might be taken care of first, but then the nurses would have to wash off the stench and grime before a doctor would condescend to examine the derelict. And even if a bedpan sat close to a patient, the patient's doctor would walk briskly out of the room, stride down to the end of a long corridor to the nurses' station, and state; "Mrs. Smith in Room 202 needs a bedpan." The more demeaning the job, the more often the doctors called on a nurse. It seemed as if they were little boys dropping their clothes in the middle of the room, expecting their mothers to pick up after them. It has made me much more sensitive to the job the nurses have to do. The more you do for the nurses, I have found, the more they will do for you.

I could see that a nurse, with experience, could get to know what to do, yet would never get to it, even if she felt she had the wrong instructions. There's a caste system. The patients bitch at the nurses, the nurses snap at the dieticians, the doctors yell at the nurses. I could see the shit flowing down the line. It wasn't hard to look around and see who was boss. When I was trying to decide whether to become a nurse or an M.D., I told myself, "If you're going to be in a caste system, you're going to be in the group at the top, who are the M.D.'s."

I always felt that I could go ahead and train to be a doctor, or a surgeon. I guess when somebody finally got around to telling me that I couldn't do it, that irritated me enough to try.

I think it was my high school guidance counselor.

She eyed me doubtfully, up and down, across a massive wooden desk which consumed most of her tiny office. I had just announced my senior year's intention of enrolling in a college premed curriculum. A graying, single, efficient, and not unkind woman, she looked at me skeptically, as if I had set my sights on the Olympic gold in pole vaulting.

"Alison," she announced sternly, "I think another major would be more appropriate. I think you should take alternative courses in case you don't get into medical school."

That surprised as well as maddened me because I had always done well academically. I don't think she meant to be discouraging as much as realistic. The probability of my persevering through so many years of study and training probably seemed very dim from her side of the mahogany desk.

As far removed as it may seem in subject matter, home economics was actually suggested to me as my backup for medical school. At one time I had been interested in home ec (the guidance counsellor knew that) and my parents said fine. I don't think my high school would have been at all displeased, or challenged my decision, if I had decided on home ec, which I really enjoyed as a good break from the books. Periodically I would get very tired thinking of all that studying ahead of me in medical school.

A few years later, when I was in college, a professor I was very close to was even more precise than my high school guidance counselor about woman's place in medicine. "Alison," my biology professor told me, dead seriously, rather as if he were underlining the obvious, "women just don't *do* that." I shot back with "That's the most ridiculous statement I have ever heard." After that we got along very well.

Actually, this particular professor's greatest attribute was to propel his students to the utmost in achievement.

For instance, he once likened my chance of an A in his course to a "snowball in hell." I was furious. I studied for that final exam day and night. I did end up with an A, but it was really because he had goaded me into it.

I think he was testing to see how badly I wanted to go on to medical school. When it came time to apply, he wrote a very nice letter of recommendation.

As a Pennsylvania resident, I restricted my choices to the state medical schools because of the favorable tuition break which my family and I could take advantage of. At the University of Pittsburgh's School of Medicine over half of my yearly tuition was subsidized by the Pennsylvania state legislature. For out-of-state students, tuition was on a par with Harvard and Yale. In truth, I did apply to Johns Hopkins in Baltimore, but more as a family joke. I assumed the "Ivy League" caliber university accepted mostly big-name-college graduates, and I was certainly not from a fashionable school. (I attended a small, coed, Presbyterian college near home.) I never bothered to visit Hopkins and only made their waiting list. I could not have afforded to go to medical school there even if they had accepted me.

While I was applying to medical schools, I was questioned as to how I might juggle medicine and marriage, although I was unwed. It was during a summer admissions interview with the University of Pittsburgh's medical school, in the tree-lined university section of that industrial city.

The interviewer was a pediatrician in private practice, a thin, bespectacled man who peered at me briefly before directing his stare full-time at my application form. Instead of the usual university interview, I had an appointment in his nearby private offices. For the forty-five minutes before he could see me alone, I marked impatient time in his sunlit waiting room, staring hard at the mothers sitting there, the toys scattered helter-skelter, the restless children bouncing from chair to chair.

Later, during the interview, I kept wondering, "What does he want me to say?" I'm sure I was nervous. Most people are for their medical school interviews, although by this time I had pretty much settled into a familiar routine of expected questions: "Where did you go to school?" "Why do you want to go to medical school?"

Now it was: "Are you engaged?"

"No."

"Are you dating someone seriously?"

"Yes."

"Are you planning on getting married?"

"At some point I am," I said.

"Are you planning on getting married in medical school?"

"I just don't have any idea. Probably not. But I might."

His eyes never lifted off his desk. "Well, don't you think that your being married will affect your class standing? Don't you feel that marriage is incompatible with being a physician?"

I told him I thought it depended on whom you married, which I think is true, and whether or not your husband was supportive. And I didn't think it likely that the person I chose would be one to restrict me. I certainly didn't have any pat answers, that's for sure.

Mike and I were dating then. We had talked about getting married and we had decided it was probably inappropriate at that time. I knew that my parents would be ready to help with my training financially if I were single, but I was not as sure of their good will if I were to marry. And I knew perfectly well that Mike was in no position to put me through medical school.

In October, I got an early acceptance from Pitt.

It was my impression that had I told the interviewer that I had absolutely no intention of ever getting married and that I hated men, he probably would have kicked me out the door. I don't think he felt I should be married, but he probably worried how I would establish myself in essentially a male environment.

Looking back, it seems like such a simple decision to go to medical school. I don't think it's really possible to know exactly what you're getting into.

# 2

# I Was One of 4 Women in a Class with 105 Men

*"The belief still prevails that a woman must be more dedicated and accomplished than her male colleagues in order to succeed in a career in medicine."*

—*MD*, June 1975

Through my four years of medical school one of the hardest things to become accustomed to was seeing friends slowly drop out of sight because we just didn't have time to get together and keep in touch the way I would have liked. As I progressed through those years, I had less and less time for anything or anyone not connected with medicine.

I discovered early that it was depressing for a doctor, or would-be doctor, to see a patient die. I would keep asking myself, "If I had done things differently, how would the patient have fared?" In time, I had to learn not to be so hard on myself.

But we laughed a lot in medical school, too, and I was treated to my share of infamous anatomy lab jokes. A lot of sexual teasing goes on in medical school right from the beginning. Locker-room jokes. Maybe if the numbers were reversed, the women would be making jokes about the men.

One of the first student confrontations is with a cold, embalmed corpse on a dissecting table during anatomy lab. I once heard the story of a woman student who discovered a severed penis in her lab coat pocket. Undaunted, she held the preservative-soaked organ over her head and asked; "Did any of you boys lose something?"

Of course she completely won over her male classmates, so the story goes.

And so was I baited for my own share of lascivious teasing during my eight weeks of freshman anatomy. Some of the guys went up to see the cadavers beforehand, but I decided I would be there soon enough, cutting into dead human flesh.

There were ten of us assigned alphabetically to each cadaver, and I was the only woman in my grouping. We were assigned to the body of an older, six-foot-six black man. When the time for anatomy lab came, the boys ran over and arranged themselves around the dissecting table so that the only place left for me was at the shrouded body's midsection. One fellow threw back the tarp.

I found myself staring at the most gigantic penis I have ever seen. This man's enormous uncircumcised penis was swollen with embalming fluid, and seemed about a foot long. It was just lying there. I was flabbergasted and didn't know what to say and mumbled something like, "My, what big hands he has!" To the men I probably seemed like a dumb Little Red Riding Hood on the way to the wolf. How was I to know that this man was so much bigger than most men? One of the fellows told me later they had tried to figure out a way to tie a string so the penis would rise up when I was treated to my first glimpse.

An occasional professor would flash slides of *Playboy* centerfolds during a lecture while making completely deadpan anatomical references. It was certainly chauvinistic, but I didn't care. I didn't find it bothersome. I understood the pictures as a means of riveting the attention of 95 percent of the class. If they had flashed Burt Reynolds' *Cosmopolitan* centerfold, who would have cared?

I personally don't think that the main purpose was to demean women. It was the professor's way of slicing through dull medical drone and rousing his students with a laugh. Jab the students awake with a dirty joke to make them pay attention. It worked, just like the way Calleb Donover used to fart in conference for attention when things were getting kind of slack. Calleb was older than most of us, had been in the service, and used to wear his army jacket a lot. He was actually a fun guy but enjoyed shocking people outrageously. Belch and fart. Sheer grossness in its pure form.

Recently, I heard that a group of women medical students decided to turn the tables. Someone went down to the porn shops in town to find an appropriate picture of a male nude. But the pictures were really crude—like a man standing with a foot up on one chair showing off an erection about six feet long. So instead, with the cooperation of a female lecturer, they projected a slide of Michelangelo's nude limp Adam from the Sistine Chapel ceiling. There were a few titters from the audience, but I'm afraid the joke passed over the class's head.

But the women's movement has made this difference: If a woman complains now about any jibes, the men seem to understand why. A few years ago a woman who objected ran the risk of being mocked as a ridiculously unreconstructed prude, unable to shoulder medical school pressure. I think we all worried about how our student ratings would read, since they might be important in applying for residencies.

During the third year, when students begin their practical work with patients on different hospital services, some medical schools provide a veritable checklist to help our superiors evaluate us. The items on the form sometimes include: clinical performance, fund of knowledge, histories and physicals, behavior and interpersonal relationships, emotional stability, interest-industry, response to instruction, and appearance. At Pitt, our appearance as well as our emotional stability was considered part of our complete picture, an element in the student ratings. It's interesting that the more we progressed into clinical practice, the less often students wore jeans to the hospital, the more we projected a conservative, middle-class image. Don't get me wrong. There were a lot of hippie types in our class, but when we went into the wards, we all spruced up. The idea was that doctors should look neat, clean, and conservative to the rest of the world.

One of our classmates was continually disheveled. His shirt fell out of his pants, and his hair always seemed to stand on end. He was told by one of the staff physicians, Dr. Copley, to comb his hair. The next day, Dr. Copley looked at him, and nothing was changed.

"Didn't I ask you to comb your hair?" Copley asked him. "But Dr. Copley," he said, "I couldn't find a comb." It was an irreverent answer but he eventually bowed to class pressure. Some of the students got after him and told him to shape up.

\*       \*       \*

I didn't feel I had to work harder as a woman in medical school. I had to work as hard as I could, period.

My third year I was suddenly in the role of full-fledged student doctor, and I can remember taking a history on a white male patient admitted for hypertension who seemed dim-witted and confused. There's a welfare stigma, and people get irritated if you ask their profession. After a while you almost hate to ask how far they got into school. I couldn't imagine this man finishing three years of grade school, much less high school. But I did ask, and I was shocked to discover he had an engineering degree. That changed the whole prognosis. He was then about thirty-four years old, and I don't think any of us had understood the long-range extent of his illness. One of the rare but insidious effects of acute high blood pressure can be certain severe mental changes called hypertensive encephalopathy.

We were all more sympathetic to him after that. It's a terrible thing, but if you take somebody who is a down-in-the-gutter-dumb-stupid person and you say "Let's work up this guy's hypertension," after a while you see so many of these fellows that you tend to say "Who cares?" You don't do as much for him as if he were a well-respected member of society. If he were, you would react a little differently. It's a trap we all unfortunately tend to fall into.

We did get his blood pressure down some, but this relatively young man died about two weeks later of total renal failure, another complication of chronic high blood pressure. Damaged by hypertension, the kidneys simply stopped putting out any waste products.

I don't think there is any textbook approach to dying, with the questions and answers all worked out in advance for you. I've found that the worst for me is when a patient dies unexpectedly.

I remember a patient who had undergone arterial reconstruction of the leg in the operating room. Although he'd had major surgery, no one really expected him to die. When I would come into his room, I'd say, "You look better today."

"No, I don't," he would answer. His assertiveness gave me a sinking feeling. He *knew* he was going to die, and a week later he did. His graft clotted repeatedly and he subsequently developed renal failure. I had worked on his case a long time, and his death left me frustrated and sad. Why does such a young person get such a disease?

It's been my personal observation that any patient who looks you in the eye and tells you he is going to die generally does die. His prognosis tends to be poor. I wouldn't have done it then, but now, when someone says that, I mumble some reassuring words, walk out quickly, and review the entire chart to see what I may have missed. Maybe the patient's statement is related to the loss of the will to live. I don't know. But I take it very seriously, almost as a warning.

The comment which riled me the most in medical school was, "You're really going to be a good doctor for a woman." I felt I had reached a milestone when someone told me, "You do pretty good work for a third-year student." He was now viewing my level of training, not my sex.

It was during my medical school generation that women started to pour into medical school. By that time, the guys in my class had accepted each of the four of us as one of them, mostly. The administration claimed the only reason they accepted thirty-one women two years later was because there were more qualified women applicants than ever before. (Actually, forty-eight women were accepted, and thirty-one enrolled.) And everybody was ho-humming this propaganda, including us, the girls in the class. There was a lot of talk that year, and a lot of debate and disgust. I think it had come out in the papers that unless Pitt increased the women holding administrative positions, full professorships, and student slots in the medical school, the National Organization for Women was going to sue to cut off all federal funds on discriminatory grounds. I think the only reason Pitt was taking more women into medical school that year was to keep their money. Without federal monies, no medical school can exist.

My desperate hope was that the women they had brought in were truly qualified. As a woman, I know it worried me that they had gone out to beat the bushes in order to get a certain number. I was worried that the women would be unqualified, and that women in subsequent years would end up having a harder time. That was the one thing I didn't want to happen.

# 3
# I Made Up My Mind Slowly to Become a Surgeon

*"In some fields of medical specialization, such as surgery, the implication often is heard that a woman is performing an unnatural act by aspiring to be an active participant in such an aggressive profession."*

—*Journal of Medical Education,*
March 1972

As medical students we joked that orthopedists were as strong as an ox but twice as smart; that gynecologists were still trying to find out where they came from; and that pediatricians were trying to prove they were better mothers than *their* mothers.

I suppose the surgical stereotype, like most typecast roles, contains a grain of truth. Painted as an arrogant, egotistical prima donna, the surgeon (usually male) was said to hurl instruments to the operating-room floor in a fit of pique when matters went amiss. (By contrast, the circulating nurse picked up the instruments without a word.) Actually, this doesn't happen so often anymore. For one thing, the younger, more assertive nurses won't put up with it. For another, instruments are too valuable to be thrown around the O.R.

No one in my medical school ever suggested that surgery was

19

inappropriate for a woman, just unusual. I did get very tired of classmates asking what my specialty was going to be. Pediatrics? That was almost the expected thing for a woman. Or internal medicine. Or psychiatry. I thought if there was one thing I *wasn't* going into, it was pediatrics. I felt the same way I did as a child—for better or for worse—when asked, "And what are you going to be when you grow up? A pharmacist like your mommy and daddy?"

As a matter of fact, it took me a long time to choose surgery over internal medicine.

Our chief of medicine emeritus, a tall man with a military crew cut and the manner of a marine boot camp drill instructor, was an exacting teacher I particularly respected. He would puff smoothly on a cigar during rounds. Students had a brief interlude when he flicked his ashes to think of an answer to his question. He expected an almost instantaneous and correct answer. When displeased, he thought nothing of roaring directly to the patient, "YOU SURE HAVE A CRAPPY DOCTOR." He was a man of bark and bite, as well as a very good teacher. As you can imagine, the students stood in awe of him and did their best to arrive prepared and informed.

At first I was fascinated by the mental intricacies of ferreting out a diagnosis. For example, let's say a patient had an enlargement of the lymph nodes. Now, the internal medicine people sat around for days and weeks doing special skin testing to see if it was tuberculosis or a fungus disease or whatever. A lot of one-upmanship went on where someone singled out a little pearl of wisdom that he had found and flabbergasted everybody with something minuscule which may or may not have made any difference.

A surgeon looked at this patient after the internal medicine people had been trying to decide for weeks what the problem was. He came in, and he cut, and he sent a bean-sized lymph node to the pathologist. Within a half hour, he had a pretty good idea of what the patient had. A frozen section gave the surgeon a general answer while the patient was still anesthetized; two days later, the surgeon had the final pathology report in hand.

In time, I looked around and I recognized that it really didn't matter how long you debated; you haven't done the patients a damn bit of good until you find out what's wrong and treat them. I became disenchanted with not really doing much for the patient, but talking a lot about it.

At some point, I took out pencil and paper and listed the advantages and disadvantages of choosing surgery as my specialty.

Number 1: I'm a woman. That's bad in surgery. A male mystique surrounds surgery. Surgeons are supposed to be rough and tough. They yell more. They swear more. They drink more.

Number 2: I'm small. That's bad for surgery because they say you need strength.

Number 3: I like action. That's good in surgery and bad in internal medicine, which is more concerned with the care of the chronically ill. I found OB-GYN boring.

I didn't go into pediatrics because I couldn't stand the mothers. Adults seemed to tolerate their own illnesses fairly well. But many mothers felt so guilty over a sick child that you ended up treating the mothers, which took time away from the kid. And if a child was dying of cancer, I found it was much harder to deal with emotionally. It didn't seem fair for a child to die without having a chance at life. By contrast, there was something exhilarating in helping to surgically remove a nascent cancer in the operating room, and adding years to that person's life. You felt like God.

One of the more memorable eight weeks in medical school was my rotation in cardiovascular surgery. The cardiovascular surgeon there is still Dave Conaghan. A really likable human being and a wonderful teacher.

In the operating room he used to say, "You know, Alison, you really can't see the operating field down at the other end of the table. Why don't you break scrub [step away from the table and take off gown and gloves] and stand over here behind me on a stool and look over my shoulder. But before you leave, wait and feel this calcified valve. See how bad this is. This is why we're doing the operation."

Then I'd reach into the patient's open chest with my gloved hand and feel a stiff ring, alarmingly rough and bone-hard like a piece of sea coral.

I'm small for a woman, five foot two, and Conaghan is tall, close to six foot two. Standing up to lean over his shoulder took some doing. In order to get a good view behind him, I stood on a high, wobbly stool with a swivel seat. I was straining to see, craning my neck, leaning over his shoulder. Once the chair started to turn; I started to totter. For one awful moment I could see myself spread-eagled over the patient and the operating table. A quick-witted circulating nurse who had her eye on me caught me in time. (The circulating nurse's hands are not scrubbed, gloved and sterile, whereas the gowned scrub nurse, who stands alongside the operating room table and hands the surgeon his instruments, follows sterile procedures and may only come in contact with the sterilized field.)

But Dave Conaghan would turn to me in the middle of the operation and ask; "Alison, can you see what I'm doing? Do you know why I'm doing it?" He's the kind of person who sends you into surgery.

# 4
# A Surgical Resident

*"Certain specialties effectively close out women for one reason or an-other; for example, the surgical specialties have long been notorious as male domain."*

—*Modern Medicine,* June 1, 1975

There aren't very many women training in surgery, and so when I went around looking for a surgical residency I was introduced to a woman who I was told was doing well and who impressed me. Maybe they had paired us up because we were both women. The usual routine is to see someone in the Department of Surgery and then the residents will show you around and give you their point of view. Laura Peters was a pretty girl, as I remember, with long, dark hair. I remember that she was bent over a microscope looking through slides when I met her. A very nice girl. Friendly. She mentioned that her husband was a lawyer; that as a little girl her mother gave her a doctor's kit and that she had been groomed to be more than a nurse carrying around bedpans. She seemed happy in her work, and I enjoyed talking with her.

At one point her bleeper sounded its insistent electronic signal; she was paged to the O.R. and I followed her around. Although he had a very serious stab wound, the young black twenty-year-old male patient was conscious right up to the time the young nurse anesthetist put a mask over his face in the operating room and drawled, "Breathe, honey. I'm going to give you some nice fresh air."

Laura Peters, in a green scrub dress taped above the knee and a brightly checkered cap to hold back her hair, walked briskly into the green-tiled O.R. and noisily knocked over a metal kickbucket in her haste. Bloody sponges spilled over the floor. No one had time to pick them up. Later, the floor would be littered with paper packaging and empty syringes no one had time to place neatly into kickbuckets. The anesthetist had no time to count the multiple bottles of Lactated Ringer's injection to maintain patient George Hillman's electrolyte balance, or the bottles of Isoprel to stimulate his heart, or the bottles of mannitol to push his urine output. When it was all over, she would count the empty bottles.

While Cliff Abbey, Laura's senior resident, guided her watchfully, small bubbles of blood appeared under the scapel with which she made a long midline incision extending from the soft xyphoid cartilage at the breastbone's end down to the left of the unbilicus, down to the pubis. She stuck a gloved hand inside the wound to assess the damage. Cliff, too, felt inside the yawning cavity of human flesh. Hillman's bowel spilled out of the cavity over the bloodstained sterile blue sheet like ground chuck on the supermarket shelf.

"Barbara?" called the anesthetist, a dark, attractive woman who seemed to be in her late twenties.

"Yes," answered the short, Taiwanese circulating nurse, barely stopping.

"Did you hear anything about blood? I need as much as I can get, as fast as I can get it. . . . Pressure is 80. . . ."

Twenty minutes later she announced gently, "No blood pressure."

"Oh, great," said Cliff Abbey sarcastically.

"No pressure, boys and girls," said the anesthetist evenly, like a railroad conductor announcing stops.

The tension was apparent on all their faces and there was no need to articulate what they were all thinking. Now the surgeons no longer worried about the size of the incision or the number of needles in the field. They knew they were in the big time. One minute without pressure and George Hillman's brain cells would begin to die. Even if he survived, the risk was there that he might be a vegetable.

Cliff and Laura took turns pinching the aorta to stave and close the lifeline, the pulse throbbing lightly against thumb and forefinger.

9:45 P.M. No pressure.

The anesthetist looked at the pulsating green line darting across the screen of the EKG monitor. "We still have a pulse." She felt his pulse. "His pulse is about 140."

Outside in the hall, a small drama played itself out.

An orderly held a form in his hand and shifted his weight from one foot to the other. "They said if you want blood, a doctor will have to sign it," he told Barbara, the circulating nurse. "It will take fifteen minutes anyway." The surgical team requested nonspecific blood, O negative, untyped, uncrossed; and the blood bank wanted a signature spelled out on a Blood Transfusion Record.

Barbara was stunned. "What paper?" she asked, incredulously. "He's dying."

"Someone has to sign it," said the orderly, uncertainly. He was just following orders.

Inside the O.R. all available doctors were scrubbed, working with sterile, gloved hands. One would have to stop any surgical procedure and take precious time to rescrub after signing.

"Shit!" exclaimed one of two interns who had just walked in to observe. "I'll sign it." He leaned the paper up against the back of the other intern.

"Hustle, Ben."

By the time Fritz Speers, the chief resident, arrived from his home in the suburbs to take charge, as well as Dr. Steinhauser, an older, fully trained staff surgeon, George Hillman had spent essentially one hour without blood pressure and was no longer very viable.

They worked on him some more. Three surgeons—Fritz Speers, Cliff Abbey, and Laura Peters—pressed feverishly around the wound. In a complicated operation, so many hands do the work that it is impossible to say if one surgeon performed the surgery. Fritz Speers talked about killing someone in the blood bank. They decided to hold on to two 2,200-cc. suction bottles of George Hillman's blood—unsterile, but blood equals blood. The bottles stood in a lonely corner of the O.R. like spare tires. A cleaning woman stuck her head into the O.R. and wanted to know if it would be a while. The new scrub nurse (a cohort had called in sick that night) had trouble keeping up with the ceaseless demands for instruments, sutures, and tapes to mop up the bleeding. Eight pitifully small units of blood arrived in their transparent plastic packaging. Cutting deeper and exposing more, the surgeons found a four-inch wrench in the vena cava, a major vein carrying blood to the heart's right atrium. Improvising with a Foley catheter, they occluded the horrendous tear with the catheter's water-filled balloon.

"I saw a whole lot of blood filling up the stomach," Laura reflected later. "He bled into a large bump of tissue which was holding things together, and we had to cut it to get to the wound. He had a huge tear in his vena cava and there was no way he wasn't going to bleed like a stuck pig."

When the nurse anesthetist announced that Hillman's heart was fibrillating, no longer pumping in sequence, Laura extended the incision upward, curving over with the scalpel to the left between the fourth and fifth ribs, making a giant, ghastly incision shaped like a hockey stick. Laura and Cliff took turns reaching between Hillman's ribs to massage his heart, gently compressing it between forefingers and thumb so as not to put a hole in it. The internal electrical defibrillating paddles failed to revive the heart so that it would beat on its own.

("Even after we got in there I didn't think his injuries were that devastating," Laura said later. "The only thing that I can think of is that if we knew he had that injury to the vena cava we could have blocked it off. Maybe that would have made a difference. We might not have piddled around with gastric and duodenal bleeding. Maybe. But I don't think so.")

"Pupils are fixed and dilated," said the anesthetist softly, announcing one of the first clinical signs of impending death.

Hillman's head was half-turned, the eyes half-opened, staring sightless in a curious look of repose.                    ·

"No pressure. No pulse. He's dead," pronounced the anesthetist in rapid succession.

George Hillman's blood had simply emptied into his belly. Cause of official death: massive hemorrhage. Time: 11:36 P.M.

The electromagnetic signal on the EKG monitor was a straight, luminescent line.

"It's time for B.L.T.'s," said one of the interns as he walked out through the swinging doors.

They dismantled the O.R. table with the cadaver still on it. Laura sewed up the extended midline incision with big stitches so nothing would spill out on the way to the examining coroner. The intravenous tubes were left in place so that the small incisions which had been made to accommodate them would speak for themselves in the autopsy report. They would not be confused with the murderous gash of the street knife.

A short time later I heard that George Hillman's three grown sisters and brother squealed painfully at the news, and hugged close. "Sit down, Momma, sit down, Momma,'' they urged Hillman's rotund mother.

''As soon as your mother pulls herself together,'' Fritz Speers said he whispered to the brother, holding him by the elbow, ''we'll have to call Homicide. It's a case of murder now. We have no choice but to go to the courts.'' For the painful announcement, Speers and Abbey borrowed white coats hanging on a coatrack in the Anesthesiology Department office.

Later, two of Hillman's sisters were seen buying coffee in the hospital cafeteria and Cliff Abbey was heard pensively reciting the first ten lines of the *Aeneid* in Latin:

> ''I sing of arms and of the man, the first who came,
> Compelled by fate, an exile out of Troy. . . .''

I'm sure Laura Peters didn't show me out. I'm sure I spent twenty minutes bumping into one dead end after another trying to get out, because I have no sense of direction at all.

# 5

# "Do You Have Any Questions?"

*"Stereotypes are bred in the bone of a society and the stereotype of a woman doctor is a horse-faced, flat-chested female in Supp-Hose who sublimates her sex starvation in the passionate embrace of the New England Journal of Medicine."*

—*Perspectives in Biology and Medicine,*
Spring, 1971

Six months before graduation and an M.D. degree, I found myself sitting on a hard plastic chair wedged between imposing desks, officious secretaries, and bookcases where the titles of medical tomes glittered in gold. I was waiting . . . waiting anxiously, for what became an important event in my medical career: an interview to consider my application for a surgical residency in a big-city, slightly fusty, teaching hospital, linked to its own medical school, part of a Northeast medical complex, all high-rise brick and monumental structure. Although I didn't know it then, it was a long moment during which my life would take a different turn.

Buz Mallinger, a fourth-year classmate of mine from Pitt, was sitting next to me. He had an appointment scheduled a half hour after mine. We talked to beat the band, and Buz said how nice I looked and why didn't I dress that way back at medical school.

Buz was eyeballing my long-sleeved, brown-ribbed body shirt, a pink-brown skirt, dark brown hose, a pair of low-heeled brown suede shoes, and a soft, fluffy beige rabbit coat which kind of contrasts with my dark hair, and which I still own. It was a tossup between my bunny coat and an old trench coat. I'm sure that I tried to look as proper and as nice as possible and that I worked on it. I don't feel I'm the kind of person who is attractive in any kind of garb, or when I have dark bags under my eyes, which is often. When first meeting me, people are surprised by my small stature. I think they imagine a surgeon as a broad-shouldered fellow about six foot two.

And I remember I had done my hair. I was visiting Mike who lived nearby, and I was feeling good. Part of my happiness must have radiated from my face. It was a sunny, wintry day, I remember. It had rained most of the week before that.

We sat comfortably enough for about two hours, two and a half hours, maybe three, waiting for the Department of Surgery's executive officer, who was closeted in the operating room and didn't have a chance to see us.

Eventually, the executive director of surgery, Richard DeKay, strode to the door. He hadn't had time to change from a rumpled green scrub suit to the conservative business suit most surgical officers wore for interviews. He looked as if he was wearing a pair of less-than-spotless green pajamas with a white coat hurriedly thrown over them to improve his appearance. A tall, gangling man, a disposable paper face-mask still dangled from his neck. I was fascinated. Seeing someone wearing scrubs in an office seemed unusual to me then, although I probably wouldn't even notice now.

"Why don't you both come in," he asked us pleasantly.

Richard DeKay found it hard to sit and talk from his desk. Maybe it was his habit of standing so long at the O.R. table. First he stood behind his chair, then he sat on the windowsill, then he leaned against his bookcase with a foot on one shelf.

Finally, he asked if we had any questions.

"I don't think so," Buz answered a little curtly. He was furious that we were interviewed together.

But I did, and after telling Dr. DeKay that I was interested in an academic program like this one, where the staff was under the scrutiny of a university community (we joked in medical school that there were hospitals where the indications for a hysterectomy were the presence of a uterus and $700 in the bank), I whipped out my list of questions about the differences in rotations at the medical center's affiliated hospitals, through ward, private, and emergency service. Traditionally residents have more responsibility and opportunity to wield the knife on the ward service, much less on the private service. What were the benefits (salary, medical insurance, laundry, free hospital meals)? And was there a pyramid system built into the surgical program? In most university surgical programs residents are moved along, or not moved along, like competing queens in a medical game of chess. What was important to me at the time was to be a part of a university surgical program.

Richard DeKay explained that there was a pyramid system in this particular program. At the base of the pyramid, openings existed for twelve surgical residents in the first year as junior assistant residents; there were six slots at the beginning of the third year, and four slots at the top in the final, sixth year for the more exalted posts of chief resident. He said openings seemed to work out, despite additional pressure from the ending of the draft, since the surgical subspecialties, such as urology or plastic surgery, require only one or two years of general surgical training after medical school.

Some training programs take two people into general surgery the first year and expect the same two people to finish. Other positions are open for one year only to residents who have already chosen a surgical subspecialty, like orthopedics, but who must complete one year of general surgery for their training and board certification requirements.

The exact initial pairing is worked out year after year through a nationwide computer system, called the National Intern and Resident Matching Program, with both senior medical students and hospitals forwarding their ranked preferences to national computer headquarters in Evanston, Illinois, by January 14 of each year. The shortage of U.S. medical graduates is such that some 4,500 hospital positions go begging after this matching, to be filled in part by medical students from abroad.

In the spring, my class received simultaneous notice of the computer matches. We strained to hear our names called in a packed conference room, and ignored the refreshments carefully laid on a table in the middle of the room. We tore open the pastel envelopes like sharks on a feeding frenzy. I found I would be a part of Dr. DeKay's program. (Buz was accepted elsewhere.)

Later I discovered that on July 1, when my residency began, out of twelve places that first year, I would be the only woman.

The stipend for a first-year resident was $10,500 a contractual year, plus free uniforms and their laundering, and Blue Cross and malpractice insurance.

I never figured out my salary by the hour, but I'm sure that with all the hours I worked, it must have broken down to something like 50 cents, the same amount I had earned as a young girl baby-sitting. At the time, my salary sounded like a lot of money to me.

In June I graduated from medical school, the next day was my twenty-sixth birthday, and the day after I got married. Mike and I toasted our union with champagne and joy. I never truly knew if I was going to marry Mike until I heard him say, "I do."

To our friends Mike joshed that he married me for my moneymaking potential, and that he waited to make sure I'd make it through medical school.

# Part II

# ALISON MERRILL, M.D., PHYSICIAN AND SURGEON

*"Ten years ago women doctors were outcasts from the female role. Now they have the womanly side; I don't want to say 'sex objects' because that's a chauvinist term."*

—A surgical resident,
age thirty

# 6
# Learning the Ropes: Not a Very Smart Nurse, but an M.D.

Excited, delighted, overwhelmed . . . and scared. Alison Merrill feels a heady cocktail of emotions at the start of her life as a surgeon. "Somehow, on the last day as a fourth-year medical student, the world still considers you dumb and unknowledgeable. And suddenly there you are the next day with an M.D. after your name and a degree in your hand, and you are expected to know everything about medicine. It would be much easier on everybody, the people training you and the patients, if you did. But the transformation just doesn't happen that way or that easily."

She is particularly happy about one recent change. "The best thing that ever happened was to make us all residents the first year of our training and get rid of the intern and the internship year. Many surgical programs have been shortened by one year, although the responsibilities of the first-year residents remain the same. Tradition is hard to break, and we still use the term 'intern' among ourselves. But to many patients an intern is lower than anything, even lower than a medical student. At least when you're a medical student, the patients feel sorry for you and want to help."

Alison Merrill, M.D., has started her residency on the cardiovascular service of University Hospital, a 400-bed teaching institution.

In the early mornings of July, the halls of University Hospital are empty, or empty in comparison to midday's bustle and chatter. An incoming wave of personnel is purposefully fanning out into the hospital to relieve the night shift. The hospital, because it is unfamiliar to the new resident, seems of indifferent stone. She hears a monotonous burr from air conditioners overhead. A color-coded map of the sprawling medical complex is positioned in the lobby to help uncertain visitors. Jumbles of white, blue, green, brown. In time the shiny green vinyl couches of the entrance hall will be filled with worried families, visiting friends, and impatient children. In another hour and a half, neatly coiffed, pink-jacketed, matronly, decidedly middle-class women volunteers will open the hospital gift and flower shop. The lobby's green and white checkered floor glistens with a fresh shine. The hospital is clean, the staff well dressed.

A blue neon sign and black arrow in the hall point the way to the emergency registration. In the waiting area of the Emergency Room—or E.R.—a few people sit disconsolately and wordlessly on chairs along the wall outside the patient-examination booths.

After the first few strange days, it's debatable whether the new resident notices the details of her hospital setting. Her mind focuses on the fresh responsibilities assigned to her.

Alison is a new part of the "Witter service," as the surgical residents popularly dub their cardiovascular training stint. The residents consider a rotation on Dr. Louis Witter's service more difficult, not simply because he is chief of surgery and the hospital's main cardiovascular surgeon, but because he has more patients than any other attending physician.

On July 1, the very first day of her residency and, traditionally, the beginning and end of the medical year, there is a gravelly-voiced pep talk delivered by Dr. Witter, flanked by Drs. Andre and Olsen, his two partners. Everyone is pressed into Witter's small, cramped office with the shiny brass nameplate on the door. It is a meeting to introduce all the details of the service. Steve Wise, Alison's affable senior resident in general surgery with three years of surgery behind him, is there, as well as Yusuf Malik, the short, mustachioed postgraduate cardiovascular fellow from Pakistan who has completed his general surgical training.

"I think you are totally torn," Alison says of that first day, "between a dread of the responsibility in front of you and the hope for the sound knowledge and quick confidence that will only come with time."

Occasional patients might think she is aloof, but they would be wrong. She is generally mild-mannered, with lively brown eyes. Her dark hair varies between short and shoulder-length, depending on the time available to have it cut. Her professional manner with a patient is calm and thorough; at times she may show anger at a colleague. Alison Merrill, M.D., twenty-six, has opted for the potential glamour, interest, professional prestige, and financial rewards of surgery. She believes that a woman is entitled to a professional life as well as a personal one, an idea puffed up by the times and instilled at her mother's knee. A part of that vast post-World War II baby wave, she determined her course long before she heard of a women's movement.

With forty to fifty very ill surgical patients to monitor and evaluate, her days spin out in a whirlwind of morning and afternoon rounds; writing notes and orders; restarting intravenous catheters; replacing nasogastric tubes; checking changes in vital signs; working up new admissions; keeping track of each of the patients who are battling ailments from coronary artery disease to a rare heart tumor. Days blend into nights. She scrambles through dozens of EKG's, I.V.'s, blood-drawings, reports of patients' vomit and diarrhea. Once in a while, a patient rips off his surgical dressing in a fit of pain and tears.

During her first resident days, she learns her bearings amidst the unfamiliar labyrinth of wings, halls, and floors. "When you arrive in a new place," she says, "you spend a great deal of time running around trying to find out where you are going." She pinpoints the surgical Intensive Care Unit (I.C.U.), and the other surgical beds spread over three floors and six wings. She unravels the shortest routes to the Emergency Room, the lab, the operating rooms, the cafeteria, the vending machines, and the resident sleeping quarters. Embarrassed but forced to stop and ask various people, she locates the obscure unmarked doors to the nurses' bathrooms on the various patients' floors. She discovers the placement of stairwells and elevator banks. The stairs, especially. She rarely waits for elevators.

She quickly observes that Dr. Witter's importance on the hospital staff is helpful in admitting patients during a tight squeeze for beds. If three Witter patients are waiting to be admitted, while another attending physician has two, all three of Dr. Witter's patients are admitted although there may be only three beds. Clearing Witter's patients for admission takes no time at all.

For the first two hectic weeks of one very long month on the cardiovascular service, Alison Merrill centers her life full-time around a consuming hospital schedule. Mike is away on business for those initial weeks. She is on call every other night, which means a ten-to-twelve-hour day every day plus night duty every second night.

"There were times during those first weeks," Alison said later, "that I honestly couldn't have cared less whether Mike was in town or not. My night off, I just stayed at the hospital and slept in one of the rooms. I was too tired to drive home. There were times later on when I was also pretty tired, but Mike was home so I would head on back."

Home is a suburban apartment Mike managed to find for them shortly before Alison arrived to begin her residency. Their first abode boasts two small bedrooms, a sunken living room, a sunny kitchen, a breakfast balcony overlooking parking-lot asphalt. With the windows open to midsummer heat, exhaust fumes waft inside, as well as the shouting of children playing ball. The apartment's main advantage is its nearly equal distance from the couple's two jobs. Another is the fairly modest rent ($210 a month), allowing them to start a small joint savings account. Among friends, Mike may have joked that he married Alison for her potential earned income. Privately, Alison comments dryly that "at the moment it helps that I earn less than he does."

At the end of the first two weeks, her daily responsibilities feel more familiar, although she is hardly about to relax her performance standards. With a straight thirty-six-hour call schedule, she rarely feels caught up on her sleep, nor do any of the other residents.

On a typical night, Alison decides to grab a bite on the run. She has already developed the resident lope, half run, half walk. She rushes down the stairs and pushes open the door to the windowless basement with its low-slung ceiling, where pipes of different diameters edge down the narrow, neon-lit corridors. She finds the vending room, a small room with walnut-grain dinette tables and purple vinyl stools. Coin-operated machines advertise their contents: Cold drinks, hot coffee, hot foods, cold milk, ice cream. Piles of white napkins, styrofoam cups, and plastic utensils are stacked in a corner. Cold plastic-wrapped hamburgers and hot dogs in shopping carts wait to be packed into the machines.

Alison sits down at one of the tables with a cup of coffee and a bag of potato chips. She rubs elbows with a couple who sit blankly opposite each other, smoking and drinking coffee. The room is crowded, and crumbs and cigarette ashes litter the table.

A third-year medical student on his cardiovascular rotation breezes into the room for a quick snack, spots Alison, and joins her. They begin to discuss the open-heart case on the operating schedule the following day.

Frank Agatini, at fifty-four, is no longer able to work, to engage in sexual intercourse, to lift a bag of groceries, to walk up a flight of stairs, to circulate his blood efficiently. Beginning with the onset of rheumatic fever at fourteen years, his mitral valve between the left atrium and the left ventricle calcified and hardened over the years and slowly became ineffectual. Now the valve is useless, unable to close. His heart disease is complicated by pulmonary hypertension. The patient is a poor surgical risk, with a 20 percent chance of dying on the O.R. table.

The third-year medical student, with a shiny stethoscope neatly rolled in his white jacket's breast pocket, asks if Alison feels any differently after her first weeks as a full-fledged M.D. training in surgery.

Alison laughs and then pauses to think for a moment. She explains that as a resident, with a new responsibility for the patients preoperatively and postoperatively, you have to camouflage your ignorance and not suggest to the patient that you are not competent to handle whatever problem comes up.

"Whatever a patient tells you," she says, "you say, 'Yes, that's very interesting.' That's one of the tricks you'll pick up fast as a medical student and that will serve you well after you graduate.

"For instance, let's say that a Mr. Forster is admitted to the surgical floor for a work-up of lab studies and special X-rays. The admission diagnosis is 'hypertension.' He doesn't understand fully what is going on, or he is fishing for information.

"While you are in his room taking a history and physical, his steely hand on your arm and his stare stop you cold. In my case, he first makes sure that I'm not just some smart nurse with a stethoscope slung over her shoulder.

" 'Doctors tell me I have high blood pressure,' Mr. Forster begins, in a headlong rush, 'and sometimes I get this hot, flushed feeling in waves over my face. They tell me I have a tumor or something. Do you know what I'm talking about?'

" 'Oh, pardon me,' you say, loosening his grip. 'I'm being paged.'

"You run out of the room. Pick up your book on differential diagnosis. *Bedside Diagnostic Examination* by DeGowin and De-Gowin. Hypertension, differential diagnosis. Among the possibilities: flushed face—pheochromocytoma, adrenal tumor. Ahhhh! Yes.

"You walk nonchalantly back into Mr. Forster's room. 'Yes, sir. What were you saying?'

" 'Do you think it's possible that I have a tumor?' he continues, slightly panicked. 'Do you know what they're talking about?'

" 'Well, sometimes, sir,' you explain with authority, 'there are tumors of the adrenal gland which give you the same symptoms that you have of flushing and high blood pressure. I think they want to make sure exactly what the problem is.' "

In the vending room, a young M.D. glows in an animated conversation with a good-looking busty nurse. A tight white sweater is buttoned over her uniform. She listens and bites her nails while he presses the button for two cups of steaming coffee.

Alison Merrill suddenly feels a longing loneliness for Mike, who is still away.

# 7

# Cardiac Surgery: "I Couldn't See a Damn Thing"

The patient, Frank Agatini, is waiting is Operating Room 2. He is stretched out helplessly on his back on the narrow O.R. table, and the anesthesiologist is slowly "putting him under," a term which Alison Merrill says is slang for senses frozen by anesthesia. During the operation, the anesthesiologist will control the depth of Agatini's sleep.

7:30 A.M. An open-heart case. "Mitral Valve Replacement," the posted O.R. schedule reads. Open-heart surgery is almost always in Room 2, the O.R. desk nurse tells Merrill before she scrubs for the case.

Resident Merrill nods and murmurs a greeting to the other members of the surgical team scrubbing alongside her: Yusuf Malik and Steve Wise. Everyone looks alert for the early hour of the morning, the usual time when surgery begins.

At the knee-high stainless-steel trough in the corridor outside the O.R., she begins the first, required ten-minute scrub. As she works the disposable presoaked sponge into a bubbly yellow-tinged froth over her hands and forearms, she looks through the glass viewing window into the operating room. The patient is sallow, his slim body already wasted. Translucent folds of skin sag from protruding ribs.

Frank Agatini's X-rays, baldly clipped to the backlit viewing box on the green-tiled O.R. wall, spotlight a thin, convex chest, sagging shoulders, and a bloated, drooping heart, the shape of an eggplant. The diseased heart is dilated with a backwash of blood.

As Merrill pushes the swinging O.R. door with her back, careful not to contaminate her sterile hands, she sees Dr. Sid Olsen walking down the corridor toward the scrub area. He will be assisting Dr. Witter, the main cardiovascular surgeon on the case.

Holding her dripping hands up high, Merrill pauses by a small Mayo stand. The scrub nurse helps her into a sterile gown, and into prepowdered, sterile, rubber gloves.

After Agatini's chest has been washed, painted with an antiseptic solution, and dried, Malik begins to push a sticky, sterile, clear plastic drape down into the hollows between his ribs.

Frank Agatini slowly disappears from view under green sterile drapes. His head, feet, and sides are draped. Now just his chest is exposed. A square skin patch amidst the green.

Steve Wise asks for a scalpel and starts to cut a hole into the femoral artery, a large artery in the groin. Into this blood vessel he will thread a catheter which will hook to a line connected to the cardiopulmonary bypass pump.

Merrill scrutinizes the complex equipment. Forward, stop, reverse. Oxygenation drive. Main circuit breaker. Pump No. 1. Pump No. 2. Channel control. Pump console. Forward. Stop. A steel case with the mass of a coffin. The heart-lung machine will take over Agatini's circulatory and respiratory functions from his natural organs for some two to three hours.

Dr. Sid Olsen walks into the O.R. scrubbing all the while, yellow antiseptic foam running from his elbow down to the floor.

A tall, intense man, his eyes, hawk-like, scrutinize the monitors' continuous digital readout of Agatini's cardiovascular activity. Venous. Diastolic. Systolic. Green light traces on the oscilloscope screen. Bleep. Bleep. Bleep. Numbers flash by like oranges and lemons on a whirring Las Vegas slot machine.

Olsen walks out to complete his scrub.

In a moment, he reenters with Dr. Witter, by reputation a laconic and mild-mannered man. Witter rarely smiles.

Witter peers at the monitors from his station at the O.R. table and announces, "We haven't gotten him off the table yet." It is a current expression among surgeons which means that the patient has not yet been lifted off the O.R. table as a breathing, functioning human being.

He glances again at the X-rays. "Disease. Disease." It is a remark to no one in particular. A chant in plainsong.

Regulating the current with a foot pedal, Olsen picks up the Bovie electrocautery, and uses the metal tip to make an incision running lengthwise from the throat down to the xyphoid, the soft cartilage at the breastbone's end.

Smoke hangs in the air, as well as the acrid odor of singed flesh.

"Listen, I'll need the head lamp," Dr. Witter tells the circulating nurse. He dons Martian headgear with a small headlight protruding from his forehead, like a miner about to penetrate fathoms beneath the earth.

All surgeons are masked, gowned, gloved, faceless.

As Merrill cranes her neck, Witter picks up the bulky sternal saw. With the saw buzzing noisily, Witter bites down the middle of the sternum in short jabs, splitting the breastbone in two, stopping to plug the bleeding in the soft gray marrow with bone wax.

Blood bags, O positive, are carefully joined to the I.V. tubes.

Witter and Olsen place a stiff metal frame, called a sternal retractor, into the incision. Alison thinks of a medieval rack as she sees both sides of the rib cage and the sternum, now severed into two neat parts, being cranked apart into an unnatural yawn eight inches wide.

The pericardial sac enveloping the heart is carefully slit, then sutured tautly to the sternal retractor, like fabric on a loom.

Alison Merrill, assisting, is perched atop a rectangular standing-stool, her hair carefully tucked under a nurse's cap, with a good view of the supine patient's groin instead of his chest. The third person down the line, she strains to get an adequate glimpse of the heart. Every time she leans forward, she feels she is getting in someone's way. She reaches over, directing the pericardial suction catheter, a long, hollow, metal-tipped tube which is meant to aspirate serous blood from the pericardial cavity to expose the surgical theater. Since she can't see what she is doing, the catheter is half in and half out of the pericardial cavity, slurping noisily like someone sucking a straw in a nearly empty soda glass. The catheter is aspirating air as well as liquid from an operating field she can see only obliquely.

Alison arches her back to ease the kinks and relieve the strain of standing too long in one spot. It will be a five-hour operation.

Although she doesn't have a direct overview of the open-heart surgery, she does know what is going on step by step. Last night, she reviewed the procedure in the *Atlas of Technics in Surgery* in University Hospital's library.

"A lot is made in medicine," she will comment later, "of the type of athletic strength you need as a surgeon. The one who is holding everything out of the field has to have strength. It's very hard on the first assistant resident. You stand for hours with your elbows positioned out, and your arms barely moving, gripping retractors to hold open the edges of the wound so the main surgeon can do the more delicate technical things. By the time you're a fully trained surgeon, you don't need strength. Someone else is holding the retractors for you.

"I have found that you need mostly stamina. On normally quiet days I'm here at the hospital at 7:00 in the morning and on my feet into early evening."

The bypass pump, already primed with an electrolyte solution to force out dangerous air which might trigger a lethal air embolism, is ready to be connected to the patient.

Two lines—clear plastic tubes—are snaked across the chest into incisions in the right atrium, and into the superior and inferior vena cavas, diverting the blood at its entry point into the heart. The blood, swirling through the machine, is oxygenated and chilled, then forced back through the femoral artery into the aorta by retrograde pressure, perfusing the upper parts of Agatini's numbed body. Chilling the blood will drop his body temperature from a steady 36.5° Centigrade to 30° Centigrade, when the heart will cease contracting in rhythm. The heart will slow to a quiver, stifling the oxygen hunger of the heart's myocardium muscle.

The anesthesiologist peels off Agatini's eye tape, pushes up an eye-lid, and checks a pupil.

The coronary arteries feeding the heart muscle with oxygen-laden blood are blocked by a cross-clamp on the aorta. Now the surgical field is clear of the bloodstream's flooding. After a work span of twenty-five to thirty-five minutes, the heart tissue will start dying.

Witter cuts a fine hole into the left atrium and cuts out Agatini's useless, rock-hardened mitral valve. Once Agatini's mitral valve was tissue-paper-thin and diaphanous.

"Forty years from now," says Merrill later, "we won't be seeing rheumatic fever nearly as frequently. But forty years ago there was no penicillin to control rheumatic fever. Like polio, we won't be seeing as much of this disease in our generation."

Two anesthesiologists are having trouble inserting a needle into Agatini's arm outstretched on a stiff armboard, crucifix-like. Anticipating the surgeon, the scrub nurse has screwed the new mitral valve into its holder. The man-made replacement consists of a small metal ball inside a three-pronged cage, topped with a quarter-sized metal ring. When the operation is over, and forever after, Agatini will hear the clink of metal as the ball slams against the prongs with each gush of blood. "You can even hear the clink as he walks into a room," says Merrill.

Gripping the angled holder, Witter sets the mechanical valve where the heart's natural valve was removed, between the left atrium and left ventricle. He secures the valve to the heart muscle with up to twenty-five cardiovascular stitches along the cloth-lined ring. 1-2-3-4-5-6-7-8. He counts off a series of stitches circling the heart.

Witter is looping stitches multi-cells thick into friable heart tissue. The yellow-red tissue trembles slightly. The heart is jiggling, and the needle is jiggling. Witter seats the valve in its proper place, then releases the valve from the holder.

An open heart, open to the outside, to the air, to view, to manipulation.

"The patient is so well covered," says Alison, "that you have difficulty thinking it's a human body."

"Twenty minutes on the pump," calls out the serious-minded technician operating the bypass pump. Beads of sweat dot the surgeon's forehead beneath the green surgical cap.

Dr. Witter is a man of few words who, probably for reasons of personality, is not saying much or handing out very many technical crumbs. Alison takes her eyes off the field to glance briefly up at Malik. He doesn't have much to do either for his level of training and is essentially as much of a flunky to Dr. Witter as she is. Around the hospital, Dr. Witter has the reputation of giving away very few of his heart cases to even Drs. Andre and Olsen, his associates and completely trained cardiac surgeons. These men are reduced, Alison sometimes comments, to being lackeys to Dr. Witter's greater, more esteemed reputation.

"I couldn't see a damn thing," Merrill reflected later. "Not only was I not seeing a thing, but Witter wasn't saying a damn thing. He wasn't teaching at all, and he was doing the whole case. During Conaghan's cases, the chief resident would be opening the chest, suturing the heart, and working along, being told what to do and why it was being done. You learn from that, too. Malik, the cardiovascular fellow was just assisting and not really learning anything either as far as I could tell. So I stood there through this five-hour procedure, whatever it was, not really seeing anything, standing in one spot, getting bored throughout the whole thing."

"Here I am like a lump," she grumbled in privacy when it was all over.

Meanwhile, the edge of the operating field around the bisected sternum is rimmed with blood-soaked gauze sponges.

"Now we're going to warm him up," Witter says.

Agatini is lying on a heating blanket, into which heated water will be pumped as in a steam radiator, to increase his body temperature to normal.

There is an aura of excitement as his heart is sandwiched between electric paddles, one on the back side of the left ventricle, one on top of the heart.

Everyone steps back from the table.

With the electric current, Agatini's chest heaves slightly off the table in a rigid arc. After only one surge of current, the heart is shocked into sound, rhythmic contractions. Shimmering flesh has come back to life, palpitating in undulations, beating in sync.

Concerned and watchful, Merrill looks up at the monitors to see if Agatini is maintaining his blood pressure.

Dissatisfied, Witter orders a dose of Isoprel to stimulate Agatini's heart into stronger contractions.

Gently, Agatini is taken off the bypass machine and the hollow, plastic lines to his heart are withdrawn. The holes in the atrium are delicately sutured.

"Let's have another atrial stitch."

Witter is polite and calm, unlike another cardiovascular surgeon on the service, who bellows his requests with sarcasm and exasperation. There is a bullying quality to his voice. Partly, it is a tactic to keep the nurses alert to his quicksilver surgical needs. "As a doctor," he will say, "you have to be authoritarian. That's all there is to it. That's the main difference between a doctor and a nurse."

Malik and Wise close the sternum as evenly as possible with a sternal approximator, an instrument which grips both sides of the sternum like a pair of ice tongs.

An awl, like so much carpentry, drills a neat row of holes into the bone on each side of the sternum. Using No. 26 wire, thick, strong steel, they tie the sternum back together again, locking each stitch in place with five knots. In the final closure, a neat row of stitches belies the horrendous man-made incisions underneath.

From a wall phone in the O.R. the circulating nurse has already called for an Intensive Care Unit bed.

It will be Alison Merrill's responsibility to care for Agatini on the floor postoperatively. She wheels his bed across to the seventeen-bed I.C.U., down at the end of the hall, through a set of double swinging doors. A red-lettered sign cries out: "Visitors are allowed only five minutes out of every hour." The I.C.U. is a place not for hand holding but for medical automata.

As the nurses hook lines between Agatini and the monitors, Alison sits down at the nurses' station to write her orders under a bank of pulsing, flickering scopes. Bloodwork for the lab. Because the patient has just come off the pump, she wants to check that he has sufficient hemoglobin. Because he was given blood thinners to prevent clotting during the operation, she wants to make sure his clotting time is back in the normal span. She orders arterial gases to be drawn to measure whether Agatini's life-blood is sufficiently oxygenated. She hopes to ascertain that his blood chemistry is in kilter, that the body's major electrolytes carried by the blood serum are well within the normal range.

The Pleuravac, a large, clear, tubed plastic bag with bubbling columns of water, is sucking air out of Agatini's invaded chest to help expand his lungs. The bag hangs on the side of his railed bed and gurgles noisily.

Finishing up her written orders, Alison looks around and peers at a new I.C.U. admission in a corner bed. Tubes are spewing out of the woman's body from the area of her stomach, her bladder, her mouth, her arms, her legs, her rectum. She's all orifices, natural and surgical. About fifteen in all. A transected spinal column crushed in a car crash has left the woman a quadriplegic. A university professor, she lies unaware of her fate in a comatose slumber.

It is 2:00. Before the day's tentative end, Alison will make rounds on the forty or so patients she has not yet seen, and begin noting in detail the histories and physicals of the two or three admissions who have come in during the morning.

A single, complete work-up examination might take nearly two hours.

# 8

# Getting Along: "You're Calling Me Down for This Internship Crap!"

As a medical student, Alison Merrill dreamed wistfully of joining the gods of cardiovascular surgery. As a surgical resident, she is never really happy in her new environment on Dr. Witter's cardiovascular service. "During my training at a university hospital, I thought that there would be time spent teaching us," she comments. "But what the hospital wants is nice, warm bodies to fill its slots and do the work. It needs trainees to fill up the slots. And if you learn something, fine."

One night there is an interesting, emergency open-heart case (a wan five-year-old boy with a friable heart tumor diagnosed as a left atrial myxoma), and she stands unscrubbed at the head of the operating table next to the seated anesthesiologist, with a good view of the surgical field. "I could get away with it, because it was a night I wasn't supposed to be working."

Another night, as a favor, she agrees to take Craig Armstrong's night call. Armstrong is an ebullient fellow who has attended University Hospital's medical school. He seems already comfortable in familiar surroundings. Alison likes him.

That night she is embroiled in two scenes. Perhaps the incidents sound relatively unimportant to an outsider, but as a tyro resident she is left feeling dejected.

The room generally reserved for first-year residents is one of the smaller conference rooms, with a hard, narrow rollaway cot, as inviting as a stretcher. Here the residents plop themselves down for the night for want of a better place to stay, stealing necessary blankets and sheets from the floor's linen closet.

"You know," the nurses on 5 South volunteer to Alison, "we have an open bed on the floor. There's a private room with nobody in it. We'll let you sleep there."

"Fine," she agrees readily. "That's really nice. Why don't you wake me up at seven o'clock."

At 11:30 at night Merrill is grateful. The room, besides being more comfortable than the one the residents use, is a great deal closer to the patients.

It is an amazingly quiet night with just a few calls for sleeping pills to interrupt her slumber. She drifts easily back into merciful sleep.

At one o'clock in the morning, the phone rings again. Jesus Christ, not another call for sleeping pills or a more minor request which still needs a physician's O.K. One of Alison's on-call duties is to sort the important from the trivial. "If the nurse tells you that a patient isn't putting out enough urine," offers Alison as an example, "you then try to figure out whether the patient is getting enough fluids or is in renal failure." She reaches for the phone.

A man's voice with a faraway quality crackles over the wire. "Dr. Merrill, this is the airport calling. We have a patient for Dr. Witter coming in at 1:32 from Puerto Rico. How do we get an ambulance over here?"

How would she know? Only two weeks ago she discovered the subterranean location of the lab, never mind the logistics of ambulance transportation from the airport. Momentarily, this seems like an overwhelming problem. Why not try the nursing supervisor? Merrill calls her on another line, and then transfers the call. At the moment she is chagrined that the immediate solution escapes her.

"I felt very badly that I didn't know," Alison commented a few months later, looking back. "It was too early in the game for me to realize that this piece of information is not supposed to be part of a first-year resident's growing package of knowledge."

Early the next morning, the nursing supervisor finds a small note propped on a black telephone at the nurses' station on 5 South: "Wake Dr. Merrill in Room 525 at 7:00 A.M."

The matronly nursing supervisor explodes to the younger nurses. On *no account* are private beds to be used by residents, since the beds have to be made up fresh in the morning for new patients. This is never to happen again. Never.

Merrill finds out about the row later during morning rounds and is downcast that the junior nurses have been taken to task for their personal, generous gesture toward her.

One Sunday, around 4:00 in the afternoon of a weekend when she is on call, Merrill is paged by an I.C.U. nurse. Dr. Malik has ordered bloodwork on Mr. Agatini, but the lab technician is unable to locate a usable vein to draw the blood. Would she come over?

A new shift of nurses has come into the I.C.U. As Alison walks in, she sees one of them seated at the I.C.U. nurses' station reviewing the late-day orders. "This is written in clear, understandable Pig Latin," the nurse grumbles to herself.

Alison says nothing and picks up Agatini's chart.

A young nurse in a light-yellow pantsuited uniform brushes by. "Dr. Vasquez is asking what happened, why she can't get out of bed." The nurse is making a statement, not asking for advice. Dr. Vasquez, the university professor with four useless, paralyzed limbs, has come out of her coma and is beginning to travel a long road into reality.

"Essentially you don't give a patient false hope," Alison comments to a medical student who has just joined her. "False hopes bring disappointments and lawsuits." After asking the nurses for the necessary equipment, she walks deliberately to Mr. Agatini's bedside.

Mr. Agatini has been in the hospital now for two weeks and is going through a shaky post-op recovery. He has been a patient long enough so that the veins in his arms are used up: hardened, inflamed, and swollen. Merrill feels she is sticking the needle blindly into an arm's flesh. No blood sucks back into the syringe. The patient's thrombosed vein is simply refusing the needle.

"As the cardiovascular patients improve," explains Alison, "their veins seem to swell into healthier, noticeable, three-dimensional profiles."

Like the lab technician, Merrill cannot locate a usable vein. A fallback alternative is to draw blood from Agatini's femoral vein, nicknamed a "femoral stick" in hospital parlance, a larger, more important blood vessel as thick as a man's thumb, which crosses the groin.

Once, as a medical student, Alison saw this procedure demonstrated. She knows that anatomically the femoral vein lies parallel to the strong-pulsed femoral artery, where it might be possible to bleed out two units, or approximately one quart, of the leg's lifeblood through the needle puncture before proper clotting.

It is difficult for a doctor to ask for assistance. "It's really embarrassing," says Alison, "to call someone the next step up and admit that I can't do it."

"As it turns out," she said later with hindsight, "naturally, it's not extremely difficult. But I had never done it, and I knew there was a technique as to where to stick the vein and how to insure clotting. I just wanted to make sure I did it right. I had been trying desperately to do a good job, trying desperately not to call on the postgraduate fellows, who have finished their residency and their chiefship. You try to avoid calling them for small things."

Merrill is taking first call from the patients, and Yusuf Malik is her backup. (He and Steve Wise alternate responsibility one step higher than the first-year residents.) Matter-of-factly, she asks the hospital operator to page Dr. Malik, setting off the high-pitched electronic signal on the pocket-sized beeper the residents ubiquitously carry with them. She hangs up softly.

Within five minutes, Yusuf calls back. "What do you want?" he barks.

"Listen," she says into the phone at the I.C.U. nurses' station. "I can't get blood from this guy. He needs a femoral stick. Would you come down? I've never done one."

Yusuf's voice booms loudly over the phone: "You're calling me down for this internship crap! Can't you do it yourself?" But he agrees, before slamming down the phone, to meet her in the fifth-floor I.C.U.

Humiliated, Alison looks like an animal stung by hornets. She is also angry. Malik is always behaving like this. For example, he might write "Blood gases today" on a patient's order sheet, never taking the trouble to tell her himself, waiting for the nurses to call her directly, even though he knew perfectly well that the lab technician did not draw blood gases, that this was a physician's responsibility at University Hospital. He could just as easily take the blood sample himself, the way Steve Wise did, but he was too far above her to do something like that. Now he didn't want to be bothered about a femoral stick on an unusually busy weekend, with five admissions she had yet to painstakingly process.

There are no bedside chairs in an I.C.U. They would be considered so much unnecessary driftwood. She feels foolish standing blankly waiting for Yusuf to arrive. So she decides to wait in the small private room off the I.C.U. nurses' station, a place where nurses gather for a hurried cup of instant coffee, out of sight of patients and visitors. She wants to pull herself together.

She leaves Mr. Agatini's room where curtains are always drawn across the window. Outside, a flower box of red geraniums offers an unseen splash of bright color.

Alison passes a curtained I.C.U. bed. "I'm not pinching you," protests a loud male voice from behind the private area. A nurse complains. "Walter! Have you forgotten yourself?" The man has just urinated on the floor. "No, I'm not pulling my tubes."

But Alison misjudges Yusuf's entrance, and in a short while one of the nurses, Polly Gibbons, a young woman about her own age, comes into the secluded nurses' room to tell her that Yusuf has just drawn the necessary blood sample from the femoral vein without bothering to find her. He didn't want to take the trouble.

Alison is back where she started. It takes ten minutes to control the tears of rage, fatigue, and frustration.

Later that evening she spots Yusuf in the hospital cafeteria eating his supper. He shows no reaction when their eyes meet. "He's not at all concerned with what I want and don't want," she will comment. "He's not overwhelmed with women doing anything but scut work." Perhaps he has misinterpreted her paging him for help to mean that she was asking him to draw the blood sample himself.

After picking at limp tunafish salad and drinking tepid coffee—the cafeteria case is bare by the end of the day—she makes a point of setting down her aluminum tray next to Malik at the same oblong table as she prepares to leave the cafeteria. He looks up at her without any change of expression.

"You know," she says evenly, controlling her anger, "I didn't want you to do it. I wanted you to show me how."

"Well, it's not very difficult." He is indifferent.

"All right. What if I hit the femoral artery by mistake?"

"Well," he says levelly, "it's got blood in it, too. Go ahead and take it."

"You know," she agrees, "you have a point." She should be able to locate the artery by feeling the arterial pulse bumping rhythmically against her finger. She should be able to miss it. But if she doesn't, Alison reflects, and should happen to hit the artery, she won't just draw back and get out. She'll take what's there, then apply strong pressure on the puncture point for a long enough period to insure quick clotting. Medical procedures aren't always done by the textbook.

Shortly before Merrill leaves on her next assigned hospital rotation, she is again confronted with written orders for drawing blood from the femoral vein of a cardiovascular patient. It is useless to call anyone down to help. She confides to nurse Polly Gibbons that this is her first solo attempt.

"That's all right," Polly says. "I've seen it done enough times." In the beginning of the year, many of the nurses know more than the first-year residents.

Merrill discovers that the large femoral vein is a hard target to miss. The patient is unaware this is her first try. Alison appears as professional as possible. "Most of the patients realize that you have to do your job," she comments.

Another point Merrill rediscovers as a resident is to be very, very nice to the nurses.

Tomorrow, she leaves on another months-long rotation, this time at City Hospital. "The purpose of changing hospital locale," Alison Merrill explains, "is that different staffs have different ways of doing things. It prevents you from getting too set in your ways." Sitting in a slum section of the town, City Hospital is practically a segregated hospital, where whites tend to be physicians and blacks tend to be patients. In the ward atmosphere of City Hospital, the surgical residents have a much freer hand to run the whole show, although they must cope with a chronic shortage of supplies. The surgical residents often complain of their City Hospital rotation, although they will glean experience that is not so easily acquired in newer, more luxurious, better-equipped hospitals. And a public hospital seems to receive a greater variety of trauma and other emergency cases.

"City hospitals provide medical schools with patients on which to practice," says Alison. "You certainly don't have the same opportunity to wield a knife as a resident at a private or university hospital."

# 9
# Alison and Mike

Five-thirty in the morning and Alison's alarm buzzes raucously on her bedside table. Mike turns over. He doesn't wake up fully any more and won't know precisely when she has gone. The bedside alarm is the first advance of a three-pronged attack on her sleep. One alarm by the bedside and two across the room. The next one will sound in the bathroom, where she can't reach for it as easily. She waits for the explosion. There isn't time to recharge fully with both food and sleep. So between the two, she chooses extra moments of slumber, revealing what matters most to her. Yesterday, since she was not on night duty at the hospital, she was able to be home around 6:00 P.M., and to fall into bed around nine.

After fifteen minutes, she gets up and rummages in the dark through a helter-skelter pile which has accumulated atop a wedding-gift cedar chest in the bedroom. A mustard knit pantsuit today. Dresses she saves for once-a-week Wednesday hospital rounds with the silver-haired chief of surgery, who is old-line and conservative. There is no use rocking tradition too hard in its small, minor details and exciting his distrust.

In the kitchen, she bumps into the laundry hamper with its untidy mound of unsorted but clean laundry. Mike doesn't mind putting a wash through the machine. But he deems it her job to put the clothes away.

"I'm so happy that he does the biggies," she will sigh, "that I don't say anything about the dirty oven, the dust in corners, or the unwashed sweaters. He does all the laundry in the hamper in the bathroom, then it just sits. When I see a wrinkled shirt, I don't know whether it's wrinkled because he wore it several times or because his drip-dry shirts sat so long in the basket that they have wrinkled themselves.''

She quickly drains a glass of juice. She ignores the fact that the dishes are piled in the cupboards in unmatched stacks.

Mike has noticed a physical change about her. His eyes don't miss a thing. By the end of her rotation, Mike complains to Alison that she is putting on extra, fleshy pounds. With irregular nighttime snacks and frequent nibbling on baskets of candies, nuts, and fruits grateful families send to the nurses' station, her weight has blossomed from 110 to nearly 120.

She reminds Mike, teasingly, that he might want to lose some weight himself. He is also fighting a paunch.

"Well," he answers gently, "you knew what you were getting."

Mike had grown with Alison through medical school. It was at this point that she said to him, "Listen, creep, marry me now or I'll never marry you." Because she was tired of all this wearisome waiting around, dating back to her high school years.

Blonde and mustachioed, easygoing and soft-voiced, good-looking and athletic, Mike Merrill was their high school's football hero. They were a starry-eyed couple. Alison Saunders realized that she wanted to spend the rest of her life with him very shortly after they first met back in their small-town days.

At one time when she was in her first year of medical school, they started discussing marriage seriously. After a week or so of talking about it, she realized that Mike was obviously very scared. He wasn't sure he wanted to get married, particularly since they were then living in two different cities. Mike refused to change jobs and move to Pittsburgh while she was going through medical school.

But once she had graduated, why not marry? Alison may have a bit of the romantic about her. She wanted to be with him for the rest of her life; and there was no good reason *not* to tie the knot. At least from her point of view.

Alison's mother, a registered pharmacist who won a scholarship to pharmacy school, never approved of Mike, nor felt comfortable with him, because he had no college ambitions. There was no family tradition, and a university degree was not important to him. Financially, his family would have been hard-pressed to put five children through college. "But I consider Mike as intelligent, if not more so, than I am," Alison will state.

Instead of a liberal-arts college, Mike spent two years at a technical college studying to be an electronics technician. He jokes that he didn't get any kind of degree at the end of it, just a pat on the head.

Mike's father, husky and well-built like his sons, was a supervisor at the town mill and never went to college. Nor did Mike's grandfather, a sometime farmer and mill hand. No one in the family has gone to college in several generations except for Mike's grandmother, a severe, opinionated, now weathered woman. She was their country school's fourth-grade teacher, and, for a long time, the Woman's Christian Temperance Union local president. Today, a spry seventy-seven-year-old widow, she lives alone and ably manages a forty-six-acre farm.

"She has never really liked me," laughs Alison. "I smoke. I drink. And—Good Lord!—I swear."

Fortunately for Alison, Mike doesn't get along with his grandmother either. She once asked him what he planned to buy with her Christmas money, and he looked her straight in the eyes and said, "A case of beer." That was the year Alison gave Mike a beer mug for Christmas.

Of course, remarks like that are "all Alison's fault."

Mike's sense of humor was one of the first things she loved about him, as well as the mischievous, stubborn twinkle in his eye.

"I think I wanted to impress him one night and told him I was going to win a Nobel prize for cancer research.

"His answer was something like, 'Oh, that's nice.'

"Much later he told me, laughing, what went running through his mind. 'Hmmmm!' he thought to himself, 'I can marry her and take all her money.'

"Actually, Mike never liked to talk about marriage. He used to joke that he wouldn't marry until he was eighty-six."

But Mike was working with Westinghouse close to the hospital where she would receive her surgical training. When she left for the hospital, she knew she would logically want to move in with him. Both of their parents would never have talked to them again. This is still amoral behavior in a small town. Well, maybe Mike's parents might have talked to them eventually, but hers never, they claim. That meant maintaining two apartments, although they would have lived in one, which seemed like a needless expense to both of them.

Nor was she sure how well a woman resident living with her lover would be accepted by a Department of Surgery which seemed conservative, like most medical departments. Nothing was ever actually said, of course. Much probably depended on how discreet a life-style you chose. It was just an intuition Alison had. In any case, since she was a woman among mostly male surgical residents, whatever she did would be noticed. Here was another pressure, another conflict of interest. She wasn't sure she could handle possibly controversial living arrangements as well as a grueling year ahead of her.

And so Mike decided, all right, all right, they would get married, if she *really* wanted to get married.

"If you are going to have marital problems at all," says a woman surgeon, "you are going to have them during a surgical residency. Mainly because you are sleeping away from home as often as every other night. The marriage has to be strong to survive. Sometimes when the patients are all bedded down and everything is quiet on the floor, the conversation will get kind of intimate. Maybe it's the maternal instinct that the male doctors look for in another woman, and maybe they're little boys at heart. And when they're not playing doctor, when they're not saving lives, they themselves have feelings. They'll talk about their personal sex lives. They're too tired to do it. 'When I get home, I'm so tired that all I want to do is lie down on the couch and go to sleep and my wife is up a tree. She wants to, but I'm too bushed.'

"When I was a resident, I'd just listen and say, 'Don't worry. The training will be over soon and you must have a wonderful wife to put up with all this. I wouldn't put up with even half of it.' That is my usual answer."

A young, recently married male surgical resident agrees that the training puts enormous strain on a marriage, claiming that the divorce rate among surgical residents is very high. "From medical school to residency," he says, "there's a radical change in life-style, mainly because you spend a lot of time away from home. If there are any problems to start with, they're just compounded. If you're up all night and go home the next evening and there's a problem, you're not in the best frame of mind to work it out.

"One time the I.C.U. nurses gave a party at a posh restaurant. One of the residents presented a plaque to them with emblems signifying

Hot Lights and Cold Steel. The motto read, 'Never Eat. Never Sleep. Just Operate and Screw.' The I.C.U. nurses are infamous for a lot of reasons and there were a lot of hot beds in there.

"For a man, at least there are compensations, and if things go wrong, there's no lack of sympathetic ears at the hospital. If your marriage is going on the rocks, there are other things you can do. There are a lot of very attractive single nurses who will go out with married men."

Being on call, Alison will claim, is beyond most lay people's comprehension. Even the patients in the hospital can't understand what the residents are doing there all those hours. "It's not as hard to understand as it is to live with," she sighs. "Once I went into University Hospital on a Saturday morning to make rounds on my own patients. I had told Mike that I would be home at noon, and we had made plans to go out together. While I was sitting in the I.C.U. writing a note on a chart, one of the I.C.U. patients started to deteriorate rapidly. The nurses called me over. 'Dr. Merrill. Dr. Merrill. *Please* come over here and help us.' And so of course I did. He went into cardiac arrest and we ended up coding and resuscitating him. Meanwhile, the I.C.U. located the resident who was on call. But the chief residents were unavailable. One was out flying, and one was spending the weekend in another state. The attending, a very conscientious attending who would have been there in a flash, was down in North Carolina. So by some fluke, it was just the resident, Chris Fritsch, against the world and this patient who was very sick. So I stuck around to help Chris out, making sure he got coverage while he grabbed some lunch. And when Chris came back from a quick snack, the patient rearrested, and was again resuscitated." At some point she called Mike and said she was running a little late. By the time she left the hospital, it was close to 4:00 and their careful plans had gone down the drain.

"Hey, Roberts," the circulating nurse calls, "do you know that the kids are getting out of school early today because of the snow?"

"A neighbor of mine will take my kid home." Loretta Rider's hands begin to twitch.

Schmidt leaves the O.R. table, peels off gloves and gown and drops them into a kickbucket. "See you," he shoots over his shoulder as he walks toward the O.R. doors. "Have fun." It is 9:47 A.M.

The main surgeon hardly ever stays for the tedium of skin stitches, sewing the patient back to normal outward appearances. This time-consuming part of an operation requires less skill and is relegated to

# 10
# A Typical Surgeon

At 6:35 she turns her car toward the city, forty minutes away. In less than an hour, the beltway will fill with the morning's commuters. She rubs her eyes and focuses on the bleak sameness of the highway as the exit signs slide by her headlights.

In the midst of a crime-ridden disaster area, City Hospital looms ahead in the semidarkness, a stark compound of yellow brick buildings. It is run on public monies and chokes on bureaucracy. Over the past few years the residents have periodically threatened to close down the emergency room because of a severe shortage of supplies.

She points her car toward the parking area reserved for staff. The area is still fairly deserted. Twice already she has been followed out of the hospital parking lot.

"If there was ever a time I wished I were a man, that was it," she grumbles.

As she parks and shuts off her engine, a car pulls up too close next to her.

Frightened, she gives "them" the finger, starts swearing—and suddenly realizes it is her tall, good-looking senior surgical resident from Louisiana, Dave Fayard.

He seems amused.

She is mortified.

As they walk toward the main hospital entrance, they discuss the new policy in a nearby hospital of hiring pistol-toting female guards to accompany nighttime hospital personnel to the parking lot.

"In a life-threatening situation like that," says Alison as they walk to the hospital entrance, "I think I would prefer a man."

She doesn't see the irony.

The shriveled, frosted winter grass has worn to the brown, bare earth. Cement pillars support a shelter where buses load and unload passengers. A few battered trash cans lean up against the pillars and one has spilled over. Single letters are missing from the hospital's name plaque affixed to the building's cement facade.

Passing through the double glass doors, Alison and Dave move into the hospital's immense halls past tan walls and brown doors. The cavernous halls and brown mosaic tile on the ground floor suggest a vast indoor lavatory. Outside the operating suites, stretchered patients are lined up like so many chairs in a dance hall, and the emergency room might handle up to 400 patients a day.

A housekeeping aide argues with two girls who have brought their breakfasts in a brown paper bag and plan to eat in the hallway. The hospital cafeteria is not open to the public.

The reception booth (empty now) is walled in with safety glass reinforced with chicken wire. An "Information" sign is posted side by side with a "No Loitering" sign.

Near the elevator, the signs are even more explicit, bold white on black: "No Loitering, Violators Subject to Prosecution."

The signs for the ladies' and men's rooms are crayoned on pieces of paper which are glued to their respective doors.

A policeman, his nightstick bulging under his uniform jacket, meanders slowly toward the employees' canteen at the far end of a long corridor.

Policemen routinely patrol the halls, and elicit statements—often futilely—from the fractured, stabbed, shot human wreckage which pours into the Emergency Room.

Three universities use City Hospital as their clinical training ground, alternating days when they take admissions from the Emergency Room. A patient on admission receives an identifying number from one of the university admissions desks; should the patient return, he or she belongs—for life—to that particular university service which handled the first admission.

If they can afford it, private patients prefer other hospitals, with color TV's and well-furnished rooms to receive their friends.

Once a week the stern department head of Alison Merrill's surgical service arrives from University Hospital in a starched white coat for a weekly updating. He is available by phone, of course, and takes final responsibility for the patients; but day-to-day surgical treatment is supervised by a chief resident who is generally in his early thirties. Underneath him is the spreading pyramid base of senior residents and assistant residents. The residents have traditionally enjoyed more autonomy in city hospitals, where private physicians show no interest in referring patients or in establishing niches for themselves.

Dave and Alison, one behind the other, rush up one flight of stairs to the second surgical floor. Dave hurries ahead. Crushed cigarette butts and crumpled cellophane wrappings litter the steps.

Alison glances into the patients' rooms as she walks quickly toward the operating end of the floor. There is the twelve-bed ward, and the smaller rooms with four patients packed into a cramped space. The patients stare apathetically at each other across the stainless steel frames of their beds. The walls are variations of insipid yellow or washed-out green, a gamut of faded, nondescript colors. In some rooms, green linoleum repeats sickeningly the green walls. No curtains, no upholstery. Venetian blinds, off-white, perhaps from the dust, keep out the sun's glare. The nurses' station, with its gray formica counters, is small, cramped, and rudimentary. This hospital still depresses Alison.

Reviewing surgical procedure in her mind, she hurries to the "Women Staff Only" locker room. On a steel utility rack outside are steep, pitching piles of fresh scrub suits, which she rummages through until she finds a size-small light green top and pants. It is still early enough in the day to find a size small.

"Can you imagine me in an extra-large, leaning over the operating table?" she exclaims. "You could see way down to my umbilicus! Once that was all I could find and I called John Kirke, one of my medical students, out of the operating room and demanded his medium scrub top. Thank God he's a medical student and I could pull rank!"

Because of pronounced status differences within the hospital hierarchy, there is very little mixing between the groups of surgeons, nurses, anesthesiologists, and orderlies. There is no one for Alison to chat with while she changes. The two nurses in the room look casually at her and then look away. Alison changes silently, exchanging her stylish two-piece mustard outfit for workaday scrubs, pushing up her hair into a nurses' bouffant cap (nurses' paper caps, like puffy shower caps, appear surprisingly on the more modern male surgeons, with bushier, longer hair styles), slipping on paper shoe covers over her comfortable loafers, and stuffing the metal conducting tapes attached to the covers inside her shoes. The disposable shoe covers will prevent Alison from carrying a charge of static electricity into the O.R., a long-standing precaution to avoid sparking any possibly explosive anesthetic gases.

She wraps her watchband around her wedding and engagement rings and fastens the buckle around the string tie of her scrub pants.

On the way out of the locker room, Alison plucks a paper mask from a box on a shelf above the sinks.

The male residents change in the Doctors' Locker Room.

"There are times," says Alison, "when we are talking about a case preoperatively on the way to the O.R. We are discussing what the differential diagnosis is, what we may find under the knife, and what we may do about it. And then I have to weave away at the Doctors' Locker Room! We can't continue." She would love to be able to pursue the end of the discussion. It's a little like a female sports reporter whose quarry disappears into the football locker room after a game.

Alison plunges into her operating schedule and her first surgical case of the day, an amputation, which is scheduled at 8:00 A.M..

According to a career book on surgery available in public libraries, the operating day in the life of a surgeon begins with his changing in the Doctors' Locker Room, where he exchanges a few words with other male surgeons. He drops briefly into the green-tiled, pressurized (air downdrafts sweep out bacteria through floor-level exhaust grills) operating room to say a few comforting words to the anxious patient before the administration of anesthesia. After scrubbing arms and forearms for the prescribed ten minutes, he shoves open the O.R. door with his shoulder, holding his dripping hands high. The surgical and circulating nurses are ready. As the surgeon dries his hands with a sterile towel, the surgical nurse quickly steps forward to help him into sterile gown and powdered sterile gloves. He notes whether the table is the right height to prevent strain across his shoulders. He reaches for the first instrument he needs, which the surgical nurse anticipates, slapping it into his gloved palm.

If displeased with the choice of an instrument, he will simply drop it to the floor, never for a minute lifting his eyes from the surgical field, or throw it at the nurse. Nurses wash his instruments, hand him his gown, tender his gloves, hasten to his commands. The surgeon barks, and the nurse obeys. Thus the typical surgeon is waited on day after day by women, and the scrub nurse and circulating nurses necessarily play handmaidens.

"If you drop your socks at home," says one surgeon, "is your wife going to run around collecting them? In offices and hospitals we're waited on all the time by women. Especially as surgeons, we don't get anything for ourselves. You become very spoiled."

It is only recently that women have more easily been able to hold the scalpel. "Not all surgical internships were open to women when I applied," says a middle-aged woman surgeon who trained at a New York hospital thirty years ago. "I only applied to one place and they took me. I guess I was just lucky. They had never accepted women before, and they took two of us. In fact, they didn't have hospital quarters for us and they didn't have all kinds of things for women surgeons.

"You didn't say, 'I'm going to be a surgeon.' You said, 'I'm going to get a surgical internship,' then, 'I'm going to get a surgical residency.' You just never thought that you were going to be a surgeon. You just thought, Well, if I can make one year and if I can make a second year and make another year, then I'll do it. But nobody turned around and said to you, 'Congratulations! You're out of medical school five years and you're going to be a surgeon!' The competition was so great for the internships and then for the residencies that you never assumed—*I* never did until the last day—that you were going to finish the whole training."

In the operating room Dave Fayard, at 6'4'', towers over Alison Merrill's short frame.

Bernard Schmidt, the equally tall chief resident, peeks into the O.R. to check that matters are running smoothly. He looks over at Alison. "Why don't you stand on a stool so Dr. Fayard doesn't break his back?"

The operating table is adjusted for his height, not hers.

Alison gains height by standing on two squat, rubber-tipped, stacked standing stools made for nurses and short doctors.

"Surgeons have the right to have the table at their height. Most surgeons are men, most are taller than I am. They're not going to assist me during surgery if they have to bend over the operating table and break their backs. So we can have it at a midpoint, and I can always stand on a stool. I'm used to it this way.

"There was a Latin American doctor at the hospital who was 5'1" and who refused to raise the table. Somehow he felt it was an attack on his masculinity. The result was that the surgeons hated to work with him."

# 11

# "You're the Only One Around Here Who Doesn't Look Like a Doctor."

While the patient, Guy Murray, is in an anesthetized sleep, Alison makes a V-shaped incision near the grossly bloated second and third toe joints of his right foot, jabs and slices the flesh as if cutting off a chicken wing, and hands the toes to Dave Fayard. Alison hopes that surgery will arrest a crippling bone infection which did not respond to antibiotic treatment.

Momentarily Dave Fayard does not know what to do with the toes, and he gestures, grinning, at the scrub nurse, as if to toss them to her. Instead, he carefully reaches out to her. She laughs and drops the toes on the instrument table. They are brown from the Betadine surgical scrub. Lost among forceps, hemostats, and clamps. Pieces of junk.

Alison wraps layer after layer of gauze around the remaining toes. Just a little trick she thinks of at the time. Guy Murray won't be able to slip his oversized bandaged foot into his shoes and walk out of the hospital on a fancy for a bottle of booze.

Mr. Murray is in and out of benders, in and out of City Hospital. He is a well liked and consistent visitor.

Mr. Murray, in fact, checks into City Hospital as if he were a vacationing regular at a Miami Beach hotel.

Later, in the recovery room, a painful way station in a windowless room continually bathed in neon glare, the burly unemployed construction worker squints groggily at Alison from his stretcher.

He tries to focus. Tatoos of women cover his body: a nude on his chest, a face with ''Irene'' etched in script on his right arm, a woman in a barrel on his left. Hearts circle one wrist.

Raising his hands, he shapes an hourglass. ''You're the only one around here,'' he says sleepily, ''who doesn't look like a doctor.''

Alison pats him on the shoulder. ''Mr. Murray, you're too nice.''

Alison's next operation is an amputation ten centimeters below the knee. The fifty-four-year-old patient, Mrs. Kane, is a diabetic, and her foot is irreversibly gangrenous. She is happy to lose it, hoping it will relieve her pain and misery. ''It gets to the point,'' says Alison, ''where the pain is such that the operation becomes the right thing to do. It hurts so much, the patient begs you to take it off. She's in so much pain right now she doesn't care anymore. She was complaining that the pain killers just weren't working.''

Alison begins a BK amputation, a below-knee chop, sawing hard first through the fibia, then through the fibula. Specks of flesh spin into the air. A Gigli saw bites into the bone with a whirring sound like that of an electric wood saw. Bone clippers—snap, snap—pick off the rough edges. A piece of bone flies high and falls into a kickbucket.

Bernie Schmidt, checking on his residents, sticks his head inside the O.R. door once again.

''Everything was clean when you went through it?''

They nod.

''You should always leave a little extra for a nice pad of flesh to cushion a prosthesis,'' Bernie points out.

''I agree with you, I agree with you,'' Dave retorts, annoyed.

''Fayard told me to put some deep stitches in, Schmidt told me not to,'' Alison mutters under her breath. ''No unanimity over suturing.'' She sews a flap of skin over the wound as if stitching a leather purse.

''Once I was scrubbing with an obnoxious surgeon on a really exciting service doing hemorrhoidectomies,'' she tells Dave, with sarcasm in her voice. ''I had practiced tying square surgical knots.

Since I knew how to make my own clothes, I thought it would be simple. I hadn't realized how difficult it would be with gloves to maintain contact with the thread. After I tied several knots which slid right off the blood vessels, the surgeon said, 'Are you going to tie them square?' He barely controlled the condescension. I was so heartbroken I decided never to make that mistake again. A nice nurse gave me some sutures. I went home and practiced and practiced on a pillowcase and the spindle of a chair.''

The patient, Mrs. Kane, starts to heave off the table, raising the stump into the air. Dave pushes it down. Mrs. Kane starts to moan. She's beginning to wake up. Alison loops the curved needle and sutures more quickly. "If the patients wake up on the last stitch, they're pissed off," she explains. "If we have to wait ten minutes after the last stitch for the patient to wake up, we're pissed off."

The circulating nurse wraps the amputated leg in brown paper and ties a string around it. An ordinary mailing parcel to be sent to Pathology. Label: a gangrenous foot.

Now Alison discovers that a patient who was supposed to be sent downstairs to the X-ray department is upstairs in the O.R. The O.R. nurses surmised there was nothing scheduled when no surgeons appeared in the operating room. X-ray learned she was in the O.R. and almost cancelled her appointment. To save time, Alison wants the woman sent to X-ray on the O.R. stretcher. This morning the woman complained of sharp cyclical pains in her back. Perhaps she does not have an inflamed gallbladder, Alison's original diagnosis, but a kidney infection. Alison wants to be reasonably sure of her diagnosis.

"You can't have a stretcher from the O.R.," growls a surly O.R. nurse. "That's been the policy for a long time, honey. You have to get another stretcher. X-ray has their own." Bureaucracy must be respected. Another nurse refuses to bring a second stretcher, which is down the hall about twenty feet away. "It's right down there," she says, pointing it out to Alison. Furious, Alison storms into a lab a few doors away. If the nurse won't get it, damn it, she won't either.

One of the ward nurses fetches the stretcher parked near the nurses' station.

As Dave and Alison began to fall behind schedule, Don Wilder, a jovial senior resident, is paged to start their next case in O.R. 6: an amputation of a latent diabetic's right foot. Brad Foster's toes, continually wet at the car wash where he worked, froze one day, and ugly, gangrenous ulcers developed at their base. The toes, black, necrotic, useless, were amputated earlier. But the incision failed to heal. Now the second amputation is necessary, about fourteen centimeters below the knee.

The open wound at the calf bristles with protruding hemostats clamping shut Foster's numerous blood vessels at the edge of the stump. The nurse pumps up the table for Dave when he and Alison finally take their positions around the O.R. table. The residents hold up the leg. You can see the bone very well and the round of marrow. Bits of flesh lie on the O.R. table. The foot bends back at a crazy, almost 180° angle.

Alison takes a butcher-sized knife and slices the remaining attached flesh on a diagonal, as if trimming meat.

"Say AGHAGHAGHAGH, say something," Don Wilder tells Alison. He laughs, twirling a hemostat around his finger. Both Dave and Alison have now taken over the surgical case, and for the moment he is just watching.

"Can you do it, Alison?" he asks, half seriously. "Otherwise back to the kitchen you go. That is how we want our women on the service." He grins. "Keep her pregnant. Keep her pregnant."

Alison says nothing. She concentrates on holding the skin flap over the wound as Dave begins to suture carefully. "It's considered a bad no-no to have the knots slip," Alison comments. "When they slip outside the O.R., it's considered a *real* bad no-no."

Don Wilder's grin broadens. "The instructions to the patient are, 'Don't move, Mrs. Jones. Don't move. Just stay in bed for the next year and a half.' It's called O.K. anesthesia. 'You'll be O.K. You'll be O.K.' "

Dave Fayard is called out of the O.R. Don Wilder and Alison finish sewing up the stump. Alison makes a note that the toes were surgically removed earlier. Pathology might think they were lost in transit.

After surgery, Alison decides to check on some of her patients.

Mrs. Smith, this morning's mishap, has waited so long in front of X-ray she has urinated on the stretcher. Alison tries to talk the X-ray technician into taking her patient next, and succeeds.

At four o'clock, the residents begin to gather in the surgery office waiting for Bernie Schmidt to appear for rounds. He will go over each patient's chart, commenting on the treatment and course of action.

The room has a general air of haste. Coats are forgotten over chairs, black medical bags are left open, food is left unfinished. A chalked message on the blackboard reminds: ''Be Neat and Clean, Folks.''

Kate Marra, a plump middle-aged secretary to the chief of surgery and mother hen to the residents, sticks her head inside the door and surveys the brood. ''Don't say you're tired. Don't say you're tired,'' she shoots at Alison, who is half-slumped over the desk. ''They'll say it's because you're a woman.'' Alison stiffens her back.

As the residents walk by the patients' beds on rounds, a dope addict with acute pancreatitis gazes out with sullen, hostile eyes and pulls the sheet defensively over himself.

You could say—or at least the residents do—that Sam Ferguson, at whose bedside they now stop, is one of their typical trauma victims. A bearded twenty-six-year-old bricklayer, he is incontinent, paralyzed, and impotent. A jilted boyfriend of Ferguson's girlfriend aimed for his masculine parts, shot him in the groin, and nicked his spinal cord. In addition, the .45 caliber bullet punched four holes in the duodenum and knocked off the tip of the appendix. A surgical team has already removed three feet of small intestine.

''I could have socked the policeman in the E.R. the night he came in,'' says Alison. '' 'Tell me who did it, Sam. If you die, we'll get him, Sam. If you don't, you don't have to press charges, Sam.' And Ferguson didn't even look as if he would make it through the night.''

Schmidt takes a pin and moves it up and down Ferguson's well-muscled legs, breaking the skin surface.

Ferguson lies on his back, staring at the ceiling from a railed bed.

''Tell me when you feel something,'' Schmidt says gently.

Ferguson continues to stare up at the ceiling, unwilling to say no, unsure whether to say yes.

''He's lost everything from here down,'' says Schmidt softly, gesturing from the pelvis down, well within Ferguson's earshot. Ferguson feels the end of a stethoscope—or imagines he does—very slightly around the level of his belly button.

''My legs feel like they want to move, they want to go out.''

''We don't know if you have compression of the cord,'' Schmidt tells him matter-of-factly. ''Whether this is a bruise or real damage.''

As the group saunters off, out of Ferguson's earshot, Schmidt looks pensive. ''I think we're going to have to find him a home for paraplegics.''

By the time the residents have reached the other side of the room, Ferguson is gripping his bed rail with strong, tensed arms. He heaves and twists his torso to one side. But his legs are like lead and don't move with his upper body.

Mr. Nathanson, a desiccated, hollow-cheeked fellow, is, like Guy Murray, a familiar visitor in this city hospital. Mr. Nathanson is a "dispositional problem." Across town, the city nursing homes bemoan waiting lists as impermeable as solid rock. The old man has nowhere to go and stares blankly at the hospital walls. So the residents discovered a few things—a hernia, for instance—and sent him to surgery. He is now justifiably recovering in a surgery-floor bed, although he should be in a nursing home. At age eighty, he was found sleeping in an alley with a temperature of 103°.

Mr. Roper, his neighbor, should probably be in a psychiatric home. He was picked off the city sidewalks with excoriations all over his body and two frostbitten heels. The residents performed a hernia repair and he, too, has a temporary home in the hospital. Formerly employed as a waiter, he is now unemployed, old, emaciated, disoriented, and a psychotic alcoholic. He answers questions inappropriately and urinates on the other patients' beds. He sits in a wheelchair with a vacuous grin and a green paper surgeon's cap outlandishly plopped on his head by one of the residents.

Despite their problems or because of their homelessness, a certain camaraderie develops amidst the ward patients. They become each other's social worker, psychiatrist, and friend.

"Once," laughs Alison, "I moved one of the guys out of the ward, and he was just heartbroken. We had just taken him away from all his friends. They do things for each other.

"One man was so happy to be here that he made his own bed. Another man, a boarder from another service, became essentially lost for a short time. He stayed two days nestled in one of the beds without having a single doctor examine him. He was unperturbed. 'Oh, they fed me and bathed me,' he said happily when the error was discovered."

After rounds, while waiting for Mrs. Smith's X-rays, Alison sits down at the nurses' station and completes her orders for the day. Pain killers every four hours for Foster, Kane, and Murray. Some of her patients are complaining they are not receiving their pain medication when they ask for it. If she writes orders for pain pills "as needed," her patients will only receive them the next morning. By then, the pain may have built up to such a level that the pills will act too slowly to be really effective. She doesn't want her patients wakened specially, if by chance they fall asleep, but the only way of guaranteeing they will receive medication during the night is to write an order requiring the nurses to give them pain pills every four hours.

A telephone page for Dr. Merrill. It is Mike. He says he is sick. Can she come home now? Alison says she still has several patient charts to complete. She sounds subdued, resigned, slightly discouraged. Mike sounds annoyed that she isn't immediately available.

Afterward, she realizes she will have to call back . . . she remembers she forgot to defrost some chicken before she left home.

# 12
# Death by Prognosis

"Put a red rubber catheter down the esophagus and into the stomach and then pray," Alison instructs a pleasant-faced third-year medical student, one of the two she is assigned to supervise, as she sifts through patients' charts at the nurses' station on 2 South, near the elevators. This morning, Alison radiates disgust. It is 7:30 A.M. Carol Carse, the medical student, listens closely without asking questions.

The clock over the main formica console ticks away. A shriveled spider plant no one has time to water throws its browned, withered leaves over the edge of a hanging basket.

"It's a long horror story for this woman. They thought Bella Johnson had a chest abscess and tried to drain it with a chest tube, which punched through the diaphragm. Then they punctured the stomach with the tube when they thought they were in the chest. It all happened while she was here in the hospital and she has everything going wrong for her."

Alison shakes her head. "Now she has a gastrointestinal bleed and is draining pus from a back incision." A nasogastric tube will empty the stomach and provide the pipeline for a gastric lavage in order to wash out the stomach over and over again with ice water and help constrict bleeding blood vessels.

Carol Carse walks around the corner toward Bella Johnson's room. Alison Merrill continues to turn the monster turnstile of aluminum-bound patient files, which feel ice-cold to the touch.

Val Sanders, the head day nurse, hurries to find a nasogastric tube from the supply room for the student to use, following Alison Merrill's orders. Val Sanders is tall, black, efficient, a person who does much and says little. Her face is perhaps deceptively expressionless, no smiles, no tears.

Now Alison will discharge Bruce Wood, who is waiting in a twelve-bed, all-male, almost-all-black ward. Middle-aged and white-haired Mr. Wood sits up wearily, dangling his bare feet over the edge of the bed.

"It's O.K. with you? I don't want to push you out on the street. How's your toe?" She sits on the bed next to him.

Mr. Wood has diabetes and an ulcerated and infected foot damaged beyond the point of surgical manipulation and repair. Amputation might not heal. He is, in fact, being sent home because there is nothing more that the doctors can do for him. Whether he realizes it or not, or whether he has been told or not, is unclear.

Bruce Wood looks down and peers at the floor submissively. He nods his head, ready to accept anything told to him, and looks up sideways at Alison as if she were an auto mechanic repairing a malfunctioning limousine; whatever the ravage of disease, neglect, and age, some magical manual will pinpoint all the body's precise nuts and bolts. It is a look on many of the patients' faces in this hospital.

"Yeah, somebody can pick me up."

"How about if we see you in three weeks in clinic?"

"Yes, that's all right. . . . Yes, ma'am. . . . Uh, huh. Come back early. . . . Uh, huh. Yes, ma'am. . . . Be sure and come back."

Alison pats Mr. Wood on the shoulder reassuringly before leaving his bedside.

In the hallway, she passes stacks of soiled linen and plastic-wrapped trash.

In the utilitarian locker room for nurses and women residents she dons the scrub suit, a paper nurses' cap to hold her hair in place, and paper slippers over her shoes.

Outside the suite of seven operating rooms, Alison glances briefly at a tranquilized, lonely, emaciated little girl curled fast asleep on the stretcher, a red balloon tied to her bed rail.

After a rough antiseptic scrub with a stiff, presoaked brush, ten strokes per finger until the skin tingles and hurts, she walks into O.R.

6, dripping hands held high, shoving the door open with her right shoulder, to join a group of residents in the midst of surgery. The eyes of the residents smile above the surgical masks; sheer, translucent gloves give a waxen look to their bloodstained hands. The skin and the sacrosanct peritoneum are already opened.

A slender woman's immobile body is draped in blue. Her hair spills over the edge of the operating table. Bleep, bleep, bleep, bleep. The EKG monitors give a continuous reading of the woman's heart rhythms and electrical polarization patterns. Hemostats occluding tiny blood vessels bristle from the cavity like raised quills from a porcupine. Alison already knows the pre-op diagnosis, which is terse and inconclusive: "Fifty-seven-year-old female alcoholic with obstructive jaundice." Name of the patient: Loretta Rider.

"Her jaundice," explains Alison, "is of a surgical nature. Something has obstructed the bile as it pours from the liver into the small intestine." Standing atop her rectangular standing stool at the operating table, she can see that the gallbladder is a hard, round mass, rather like a pear, tense and swollen with bile.

As casually as plucking French fries from a hamburger platter, Bernie Schmidt sticks his hands deep into the wound and pulls the liver lobes out of the abdominal cavity.

Alison leans closer to scrutinize ominous white points on the liver's lip.

Schmidt points to the small white nodules. "This is cancer," he announces.

A tumor—that wonderful euphemism—has blocked the bile flow from Loretta's liver to the intestine.

Without ceremony, Schmidt again sticks his hand deeply into the wound. "There's a big nodular mass in the pancreas and widespread disease. This patient is beyond any curative procedure. Let's order a frozen section.

"I can say we predicted this," he says, a little halfheartedly.

Alison reaches in to feel the affected organs, sharpening her surgical senses to recognize disease by touch.

"In a short time," she says, "cancer begins to feel ugly. It's usually hard. Very, very hard. It has a gritty feel to it and it just feels ugly when you're used to feeling normal tissue. Maybe it feels ugly because you know that's what cancer feels like, and that is ugly, and you make the association. Carcinoma is different colors depending on where it is. Melanoma, one type of cancer, can be black, but most cancer is usually whitish. This one is a grayish white.''

The patient starts to nod. She's waking up. The incision is still open. ''Give her one-half cc. more anesthesia,'' says the nurse anesthetist, instructing Betty Pierce, a medical student rotating through Anesthesia. ''You have to realize that an alcoholic will take a lot more. She isn't going to walk off the table, but she is light.''

Bernie Schmidt squeezes threadlike suture around a nodule. ''I'd give her six months, but she'll probably be worse than the average. We'll bypass the obstruction so that the bile will go to the intestine.'' The surgical team will take a loop of the small intestine and sew it delicately to the gallbladder.

There is no automatic respirator, and Betty Pierce keeps up a steady rhythm at the head of the O.R. table with one hand on a black rubber bag, squeezing air out, letting air in.

Nurse Roberts, the anesthetist who stands protectively behind Betty's chair, is giving her some unrelated advice. ''I don't believe in general anesthesia for a woman in labor. The child is getting all that garbage and there haven't been any follow-up studies. You don't know if the child can't read at four or five because of that. It goes right into the circulation and bloodstream and into the placenta. I had eight pounds and six ounces worth of natural childbirth. There are some hospitals where they still give general anesthesia for delivery.''

Alison decompresses the gallbladder with the help of a suction catheter. With a steamlike hiss as from a leaking radiator pipe, brown-green bile streams through the transparent suction tubing into a plastic container, and the turgid gallbladder becomes pink and flaccid.

A jarring electronic voice blasts shrilly over the loudspeaker into the O.R. quiet: ''Is Dr. Merrill there?''

''Yeah? What do you want?''

With the delivery of a short-order cook shouting from a back kitchen, a disembodied pathologist dishes out his verdict in monotone: ''Fro-zen-sec-tion-ma-lig-nant-prob-ably-pan-creas.'' Just another routine, straightforward presentation of the facts.

Cancer was born when life was born, but no one knows how the bad seed lodged in Loretta's pancreas. The malignant cells were there, eroding the living pancreatic tissue, growing and pushing everything out of their way, crushing against the bile duct where it passes briefly through the pancreas so that the bile backed up and choked the liver with its own byproducts.

A surgical procedure that might have produced a cure has tendered a death sentence. Opening up Loretta Rider is like gazing into the crystal ball of her future.

"Thank you." Alison's message will carry back to the pathologist over the intercom set into the tiled O.R. wall. Amenities are simply an acknowledgment of message received.

"Talk about good hard muscles," the nurse anesthetist tells the medical student, who continues to punch the respirator bag, "you could strangle anyone after this."

"Sponge," asks Schmidt of the scrub nurse.

The high-pitched scream of a small child intrudes shrilly into the O.R.

Bypassing the growth of runaway cells, the curved needles loop over and over again into the gut.

Bleep, bleep, bleep and the scream of a terrified child.

A blue electrocardiogram dot bounces up, down, and across the monitor screen.

"For the record, what would you like to call this exercise?" nurse Roberts asks casually. After instructions from Schmidt she writes "cholecystojejunostomy" on the O.R. sheet. Loretta Rider shakes her head from side to side. "Give her 2 ccs.," orders the anesthetist evenly.

Alison flushes out the wound with saline from a syringe. Blood and water spill out and are caught by a drape. The skin around the wound has stretched into thin wrinkles. With forceps in one hand, and a needle clamped into a metal holder in the other, she begins to sew up the layers of fascia.

"Hey, Roberts," the circulating nurse calls, "do you know that the kids are getting out of school early today because of the snow?"

"A neighbor of mine will take my kid home." Loretta Rider's hands begin to twitch.

Schmidt leaves the O.R. table, peels off gloves and gown and drops them into a kickbucket. "See you," he shoots over his shoulder as he walks toward the O.R. doors. "Have fun." It is 9:47 A.M.

The main surgeon hardly ever stays for the tedium of skin stitches, sewing the patient back to normal outward appearances. This time-consuming part of an operation requires less skill and is relegated to junior residents, sometimes medical students, to beef up their training.

"An operation takes four or five hands nowadays," says Alison. "And it is sometimes hard to say who is doing the operation. It's a team effort. The person who holds the knife is not necessarily the one who does the operation. An older, more experienced surgeon may be directing a resident's scalpel, telling him where to cut and where to suture. Many hemorrhoidectomies and hernias at university and city hospitals are performed by first-year residents. On the other side of the picture, it's not really fair for the medical graduate to go out and practice on the general public without formal training and supervision by a fully trained staff. But the public hasn't accepted that yet and it's just glossed over to the patient."

"Let's not dilly-dally," chides Dave Fayard, who will now take over for Bernie Schmidt. "She's not in super shape."

"Either alcoholics take next to nothing and sleep forever or they take a big dose and bat their eyelashes at you," nurse Roberts warns her all-ears medical student. "This one, for someone in her condition, took a good bit."

The wound starts to bristle with royal blue synthetic suture. Alison is careful not to tie the ends of her gloves into the knots. (It happened once before.) Yellow globular fat peeks out from under the skin stitches. Alison dabs the wound dry with a towel.

Dry, stitch, dry, stitch. The transverse gap grows narrower, the cavity is closing.

"Symptomatically," says Dave, "she'll feel a lot better, but the long term is death. She'll be able to go home for a little while."

Loretta's twisting hands are outstretched and strapped to the table. The cruciform figure seems to want to rise from under the drapes like Lazarus lifting from the dead.

"If she were uncomfortable," says Roberts, unimpressed, "she'd be screaming."

Patiently Alison instructs John Kirke, her medical student, who stands opposite her, on the techniques of tying surgical knots: "The knot should be perpendicular to this incision. If you lay it down this way, the stitch pulls flat. Push the needle down so it bites into several layers of fascia. That's good. That's nice and even." Blankly, he follows her instructions silently.

Knot, tie, snip.

Loretta Rider is beginning to wake up. Alison and John Kirke are still sewing.

"It's like this," says Alison, looking up from the field. "Later, what impresses the patient is the look of the scar. 'Oh, I have such a good doctor. Dr. Witter is such a good surgeon. Look at the way my scar is healing.' What they don't know is that the medical students often do the skin sutures.

"In America, people hold very strong and fast to the freedom of choice of their doctor. But the reasons why they choose their doctors often have nothing to do with the doctor's technical skill. Although I'm still learning, I once had a patient who agreed to a second surgical procedure because he liked the skin closure that I had done on the first. And I told him I would be present in the O.R. for the second one."

Alison bends over toward the anesthetist. "We're on our last stitch."

Some blood bubbles over the wound. Loretta Rider opens her eyes. Alison rubs a towel over the wound. Loretta sways her head back and forth. Alison begins to position a sterile gauze dressing over the incision. The body which has been sallow, yellow, and inert begins to move.

"OPEN YOUR MOUTH, OPEN YOUR MOUTH," shouts Roberts authoritatively. "THE OPERATION'S ALL OVER. WE'LL TAKE YOU TO THE RECOVERY ROOM, O.K.? Now, Dr. Pierce, you have to take the blood pressure."

They slip a small white hospital top on the patient's nude, now undraped body. 10:40 A.M., finishing time.

How will Loretta Rider find out about impending death? Not in the recovery room, where several post-op patients lie with more or less stunned, anesthetized senses on high, railed stretcher-beds. Alison sits on top of the nurses' desk in a green scrub suit, her legs over the side, about to formulate Loretta Rider's medication orders and dictate them to John Kirke, standing beside her.

"You should tell a patient in stages," says Dave Fayard. " 'You have a tumor.' People don't want to know any more. They don't want to know too much." Dave chops the air with his hand. " 'We can do something for you. We can give you drugs to deaden the pain.' It's too depressing long-term." He winces. "You desex a person, mutilate them, or chop their arm off like a candy bar. I wouldn't want to handle cancer patients all the time. It's depressing for the doctor if most of his patients die.''

Loretta starts to moan. Dave walks over to her stretcher.

''I wouldn't want to addict Brad Foster on pain killers,'' Alison tells John, ''but with Loretta Rider it wouldn't matter as much. Cancer is a painful and ugly death. People have a suspicion they may have cancer, but they don't really want to hear it. However, you don't want to make them completely pain-free. Pain lets them know they're still alive. They're afraid if they go to sleep at night they won't wake up. So what if you addict someone who's dying?''

Alison dictates while John notes the post-op medical orders. Vital signs, activities, intravenous tubes and drains, diet supplements, lab work. The seven Ps, the medical students jocularly call the post-op orders. Piss, pulse, palate, pain, position, previous orders, and pipes. Not necessarily out of disrespect, but to help them jog their memory. John listens and writes stiffly and self-consciously.

Loretta starts to moan. ''TAKE SOME DEEP BREATHS. COME ON, IN AND OUT,'' a nurse shouts through Loretta's scrambled senses.

''Better get an EKG,'' Alison instructs John without changing her pace, outlining Loretta's orders and teaching him as well. ''We'll give her some Librium so she doesn't go into D.T.'s. The in-hospital mortality rate for delirium tremens is very high, 10 to 12 percent.''

No time for lunch. Just a bag of potato chips on the fly from the employee's canteen, where a group of maintenance men in coveralls are taking a break.

Alison is philosophical. ''I have no hesitancy in giving direct orders when I have to. It just snaps out. But I worked out a long time ago that men don't like to take direct orders from women. So I rarely give a direct order to any of the men regardless of what their position is. At first I started out saying what a resident taught me in medical school: 'If I were you. . . .' But that sounded too false. Now I say, 'What do *you* think?' 'Do *you* think that such and such, this particular blood test, might add something to your information?' There's a whole hierarchy. The older residents literally try to shove it down the throats of the younger ones. 'This is what I had to go through; this is what you're going to go through.' But you can catch more flies with honey than with vinegar.''

# 13
# Why Me?

At the drab nurses' station on 2 South, Val Sanders talks to Alison in hushed tones. Bella Johnson is not responding to treatment.

"She's gurgling," says the head nurse.

Alison looks hard at her. "Did you check if the tube is put in right?" She whispers, "One of our medical students did it, you know." The tube may be coiled at the back of the throat.

Bella Johnson never opens her eyes as Val Sanders and Alison march into her room to check whether the rubber tube is properly threaded into her left nostril, down her throat, into her stomach. Her son, seated at the window—a tall, good-looking, twenty-year-old dude with a wide-brimmed hat, leather boots, and a sole gold earring —smiles inappropriately at the fuss surrounding his mother.

Alison ignores him. Her pace is often too rushed, the work too urgent, to include the social amenities in her care. "Swallow for me, honey," Alison asks of her patient.

No response. No perceptible movement. Bella Johnson is propped up with pillows to a half-sitting position. Her mouth hangs open. During the whole examination she neither opens her eyes nor moves her head from her pillows.

Her son never stops grinning.

Later, during afternoon rounds conducted by Bernie Schmidt, Bella Johnson becomes the eye of a medical whirlwind.

It is 5:00 and snow has cloaked the hospital. Wind-suspended billows of white fluff obscure nearby buildings. Outside, a group of visitors and off-duty daytime staff stand in dimmed light, ankle-deep in soft snow, shuffling to keep warm, waiting for the headlights of a long-delayed, off-schedule city bus.

Bella Johnson is alone now and seemingly comatose. Her son has gone home. Her head has not swerved from its fixed position on the pillow stack since this morning. That a group of six residents and a scattering of medical students have just walked in to ponder her present, and decide her future, makes no difference.

Her medical facts are presented in the solemn textbook fashion expected of rounds. "Bella Johnson," says Alison, "has a subphrenic abscess just below the diaphragm. She was doing very well until convulsions set in. Her abscess started on the left side and now it is on the right. It may be that the abscess was not drained completely the first time. She has a possible brain hemorrhage."

The residents debate where they would have made the initial incision, "if you had to do it over again." There are six different spots where they might have placed the drainage tube. Alison says that she has no brain scan on Bella Johnson, and although Schmidt makes no comment, she senses that he is very unhappy.

A brain scan is a diagnostic procedure in which the patient is first injected with a compound containing a radioisotope. Eventually the radioisotope swims to the brain, where the radioactive material tends to collect at the site of a lesion and is detected by a scanner.

All points are made and facts debated in front of the patient.

Bernie pokes Bella Johnson's bare arm, and she seems to shudder all over as if chilled by a cold blast. It is her first sign of movement.

"I think she's septic," says Bernie, who suspects a generalized infection feeding into the bloodstream.

He decides to operate in order to ensure that the abscess will be drained and blotted completely. Don Wilder smiles and shakes his head at the end of their discussion during rounds. "Medicine is not an exact science," he comments wryly. It is hard to tell what the decision would have been had they been able to predict that their patient would die that night.

Antibiotics are as useless as a finger in a dam to counterattack such a massive infection. "There you are, between the devil and the deep blue sea," says Alison as she leaves Bella Johnson's room. "Will she or will she not seize on the operating table? We can't envision getting her into better shape with antibiotics."

Bella Johnson cannot ratify the residents' decision. Alison must first obtain the family's signed permission for the surgery. Reached at home by phone, Bella Johnson's married daughter squirms at the idea of making a life-or-death decision, and defers to her brother. She doesn't want to have the responsibility for the outcome on her conscience.

Reached in turn, the brother is more nonchalant. "Well, you know what's best," he says.

That night, after the emergency operating procedure, Bella Johnson convulses pitifully and loses whatever questionable hold she has on life. The surgical I.C.U., where beds are crammed into close quarters, won't accept Bella Johnson because her system is contaminated with pus. Hours later she has no pulse, no blood pressure, and her eyes are fixed and dilated. She suffers a heart attack. Her body is fighting and losing to a generalized massive insult from the surgical draining of the abscess.

"The squash is gone," Alison mumbles, using neurosurgeons' slang for the slimy, amorphous brain.

Sometime during the evening she calls Mike. "How are you doing?" she asks. Just a brief chat, without any gruesome details.

"Sometimes I think Mike has trouble picturing what I do," she sighs, hanging up. "I don't think he can envision me in any role except as a real *dummkopf.* At home I burn the corn, neglect the laundry, and forget to defrost something in time for supper.

"Mike has a low comprehension of what goes on at the hospital, doesn't understand the intricacies, and probably isn't interested. I don't usually talk about the patients at home. Maybe I might mention that someone is giving me a hard time, or that some event is upsetting me.

"The outstanding events in my surgical career probably wouldn't seem outstanding to Mike. He, or any uninvolved layman, would have a hard time comprehending why my remarkable surgical moments are so out of the ordinary. Like a first appendectomy or my first gallbladder.

"Once, at University Hospital, I examined a normal, healthy twenty-six-year-old man with appendicitis. He had no insurance, which meant he was a house case, and he was going to be *my* case. House appendectomies are usually given to the first-year residents. He was in pain but I was also in pain. My first big case of the year and there was not a bed in the house.

"I was just so upset I could have cried. I wanted to operate on him and keep him post-op on a stretcher in the Emergency Room, but the hospital would never have agreed. I reluctantly saw my prospective patient shipped by ambulance to another hospital nearby.

"One woman, also a house case, arrived at the E.R. around midnight and was slated for a gallbladder removal and common bile duct exploration for stones. And I had never done a common bile duct exploration. I could just see that case. Not one bed.

"I went so far as to prowl from floor to floor to make sure that there were two patients in every semiprivate room and one patient in every private room. Every single room I walked into had a patient. I was so mad. I knew there would be several patients discharged the next morning, but the hospital would not have let me keep that lady in the E.R. until 7:00 A.M.

"I thought it was a little crude to throw out a patient at midnight. But I contemplated it. I had a patient going home the next day and I really pondered calling him and saying, 'I need your bed. Would you mind leaving tonight?'

"Mike, or anyone, might wonder why an appendectomy or gallbladder removal was so important. But both cases are slightly harder operations, and the chief resident was going to let me do them.

"Mike probably thinks I can perform all right as a surgeon, but he can't really visualize me doing it. He has never come to see me at the hospital. And it would be hard for him to do so at the moment because he's working the night shift at Westinghouse."

Sometime during the night she calls the Johnson family and asks them to come into the hospital. "I never tell someone on the phone that a family member is dying. Instead I say he or she is in critical condition. Can they come to the hospital? I can't imagine what might happen, but it scares me to tell someone who might be alone."

At 9:00 the next morning Alison's face is blank with fatigue. She sits at the nurses' station making final notes on Bella Johnson's chart. The nurses have scurried to find a shroud, and the morgue tag is ready and tied to a sole uncovered toe. Bella Johnson's skin already seems to be changing color toward a sallow yellow. It is considerably before regular visiting hours, which begin at noon. A matronly, well-dressed woman strides up to the second-floor nurses' station on the heels of the floor nurse. The visitor has taken pains with her appearance. She wears a hat and gloves, and carries a brown leather purse which matches her shoes.

"Where is Mrs. Johnson?" asks the woman of any one of the nurses.

"Who are you?"

"I'm her sister."

A nurse wears a look of horror. "Dr. Merrill, this is Mrs. Johnson's *sister*," she whispers quickly to Alison. "Do you want to talk to her?"

The woman takes her cue from the nurse's confusion and Alison's stunned expression. "Please tell me she hasn't died! She hasn't died, has she?" the woman wails.

"I'm sorry," Alison blurts out. "But she was critical. But she is dead."

"Why wasn't I called?" the woman protests loudly.

"I called Mrs. Spencer, your niece."

"But I don't have a niece!"

Both women are speechless. It is hard to say who is more dumfounded. It is a case of similar names, same time, wrong place. The woman has started her day on the wrong floor, in the wrong unit, with the wrong patient.

You might think that she would be furious. But she is a gentle person and ecstatically happy, with a kind of rebound effect of joy, made even more precious because her sister wasn't dead yet, after all.

"The poor woman was hysterical," Alison says later over rushed morning coffee. "I feel terribly to have put her through such an experience. But with that name, it never occurred to me she was asking for another patient."

Even a sordid scene has its tragicomic moments. And being up all night exacts its price.

Later, Alison, in the ubiquitous green scrubs, her stethoscope slung precariously over her shoulder, sits quietly on the edge of Loretta Rider's bed. "Has Dr. Fayard talked to you about your disease?"

Loretta wears a pink cotton nightgown and looks slim and girlish for her fifty-plus years. "Dr. Fayard told me I had a tumor," she says matter-of-factly. "He said that some specialists would come in to see me."

"Let me tell you what they told us." Alison pauses. She speaks gently, choosing her words carefully so as not to frighten the patient, yet also to let her awareness of her true condition sharpen. She assesses Loretta Rider's reaction to her words, watching for any sign of hysteria.

"The tumor cannot be taken out surgically. Once it has spread all over, we cannot take it out. There are drugs we can give you for the pain. In about three weeks you can begin to take drugs to retard the growth of the tumor."

"It won't go away?" Loretta looks up sharply at Alison.

A gentle "No."

Loretta hangs her head, staring down hard at the white sheet in confusion.

"That means it might grow faster, too, then." She pauses, looking at Alison. "If you can't do anything from surgery now, you can't do it later."

Loretta doesn't seem to expect an answer. She turns and looks through the window at the leafless trees.

"Oh!" she says, in a small, pinched voice, and presses her fingertips into her skull, stunned with the enormity of it all.

Alison will use the word "cancer" only in a few days' time, when Loretta Rider is over the major postoperative pain. But she is preparing Loretta that the future is death.

"You can go home pretty soon. Is there anyone who can stay with you? Your mother-in-law?" Alison knows, but does not mention, that Loretta is in the process of a divorce and that her husband has not even appeared to see her. Loretta's mother-in-law is worried that she will start drinking again if left alone, but has not offered terminal shelter.

Loretta Rider seems to regain some composure and becomes suddenly businesslike. "My youngest son is away at school and my other son lives in an efficiency and doesn't have room. One thing I don't have is heat in my house. My furnace broke down and I don't have any money to fix it. My electric heater costs $75 a month and I won't use it."

"We can't really let that happen. We can't send you home to a cold house. I tell you what. Tell your son to come see me when he arrives."

Outside in the corridor, out of earshot, Alison shakes her head. "There's a whole psychology to dying. Sometimes they'll say, 'Why me, God? I haven't done anything wrong.' Basically, to be diseased is still perceived as punishment from God.

"I'll speak to my social worker," Alison decides, "the one who talks to all my patients. I don't know how she does it, but somehow she digs up the funds. Somewhere there are community resources to fix the heater, to arrange for visiting-nurse service or housekeeping."

She goes briefly to see Sam Ferguson, who is now out of the I.C.U. and in the surgical ward. He looks wan and less confident than before and complains about the nursing care. "It's not even special care, it's no care. I'm not really getting care here." He is close to tears.

Alison is conciliatory. "If you don't think that you're getting proper care here, we'll transfer you to University Hospital."

"There's not even a paraplegic ward here. There's very little I can do for myself."

Alison looks at a bouquet beside his bed and tries to change the subject.

"My apartment is filled with plants and flowers," says Ferguson.

"I took the ivy from my bridal bouquet," Alison says, "and it died on me. I did everything to keep it alive."

Ferguson smiles. "You've got to *sing* to it."

When Alison leaves for the day, taking the gray hospital elevators, which look like freight elevators, the doors open at a lower floor and she spies the other Mrs. Johnson's sister, who waves warmly in a flash of recognition. Alison seems pleased. "At least I made somebody happy today," she muses.

A few days later during an evening when Alison is on duty, Loretta Rider's college-educated son arrives and asks to speak to Alison, who has been steeling herself to break the news.

They talk in a small conference room off to the side of the nurses' station, a room of streaked arm-desks and drab yellow walls.

The son is a good-looking, talkative young man who wears a red Shetland sweater and beige corduroy jeans. He looks strongly built and determined.

They sit opposite each other, and Alison tells him that his mother has cancer and that chemotherapy does not offer any cure. "She'll have to have somebody living with her," Alison explains. "She'll feel better, then start to go downhill. She'll start to lose weight and get weak. The average person does better outside a hospital."

"She's not the average person," the son retorts brusquely. "She does better in a hospital. She goes back to drinking again when she's home. Only this time it will end in the grave."

"Has she been a problem?"

"Oh!" The son looks up at the ceiling and sighs disgustedly. "A long, long problem for many years." He seems to be saying that the cancer is only one insult in a series of insults. "Well, we all thought she was going to drink herself to death, but I guess she won't have time for that, will she?"

Alison stares in disbelief, momentarily speechless. The son has not asked how long death will take nor how painfully it will come. He doesn't seem interested in knowing. Loretta Rider is an alcoholic dying of cancer and her son shows no regret.

Alison is not sure the son understands, and tries to be more specific.

Then they talk about the lack of heat in Loretta's house.

"She's refused to budge out of that house," says the son. "There's nobody that she wants to live with. If there's someone who wants to live with her, I don't know."

"She has to have somebody with her all the time."

"Well, we'll find somebody for her," Loretta Rider's son says as he leaves the room without further concern.

Alison is shaken.

"The conversation sent a chill through me," she reflects later. "It was almost as if he were trying to say, 'Why are you invading me with this problem? My mother has been such a pain in the ass to me and now she's doing this.' Usually people try to hide such hostility to their parents. It's really heart-rending—Loretta Rider looks like such a nice pathetic older lady and her son thinks she's a bitch.

"The family vary rarely shows that to you. And usually the families of terminal alcoholics are the most demanding of you. They want so much to get rid of their bothersome relative and they feel so guilty about it. They repress it and they need a scapegoat. They need someone to put the blame on while they hope to hell he'll go. So they'll put the blame on you, the physician, and make constant impossible requests.

"In medical school we were told about the five stages of dying described by Dr. Elisabeth Kübler-Ross. Denial, anger, bargaining, and depression. The final stage is acceptance. But there's just no way they can tell you *how* to tell the patient, the relative, the mother, the brother.

"It's not something they can teach you."

# 14

# What Is Feminine Medicine?

In the early afternoon during surgery clinic where six residents and five medical students will see eighty to ninety patients within three hours, Don Wilder throws his arms good-naturedly and protectively around Alison. "She hasn't let her femininity stand in the way," he teases. "She cusses just like the rest of us."

Alison looks up at him, and meets his eyes, and laughs.

"She makes a really good roommate. She doesn't mind if you hang up your socks. She gives you candy. She answers your phone. And she wears Estée Lauder perfume."

"I can't let my femininity stand in the way," says Alison later. "For instance, I never knock when I come into the second-floor office in the morning. I might find one particular resident standing there in his underwear shaving, having just spent the night on call. I'll ignore his informal attire and we'll just start talking about the patients as if there were nothing unusual."

Bernie Schmidt walks up and pulls at the lapels of Wilder's white coat. "Hey, do you have these custom-made?"

Wilder grins. He has a reputation for being dapper and spendthrift.

"How about that Mercedes Benz? Have you bought it yet?"

He nods. "Sure."

Schmidt is disbelieving. "Some woman is going to take you for the biggest ride."

Wilder is still grinning.

"Come on." Hank Sanchez swats his female medical student on the fanny with his stethoscope. The medical student, Julie Lauer, smiles weakly. Hank Sanchez, a first-year resident, wears a see-through navy blue shirt with white pinpoints.

"I wore an undershirt today so I wouldn't shock Julie," he jokes as they move toward an assigned booth.

Alison joins Dave Fayard, who is seated at a small table covered with a scattering of patients' files. "Look at this," he says to her disgustedly. "A guy with a million problems all interrelated. He's been in and out. His file is four inches thick with no summaries. The other day I had an X-ray where you couldn't even find the heart. Sometimes the photographs at this hospital are so bad they're completely useless."

"One time at Pittsburgh we got a blank X-ray," Alison offers in agreement. "The guy did it on purpose. It was $50 if we called him back."

Alison looks at the forms spilling out helter-skelter over the table. She reaches through and picks up a folder, then passes it to Kirstin Fernie, a third-year medical student in white hip-huggers, with long, frizzy hair and a handwoven Greek bag slung over her shoulder.

"See One, Do One, Teach One," Kirstin mutters as she heads toward her patient, waiting behind a gray curtain, only his feet visible. "That's the motto of our medical school. Sometimes you're lucky to Do One in between or See One before you Teach One."

After a few minutes Kirstin makes an unusual theatrical exit from the curtained cubicle. Putting on a dramatic act, she addresses the residents waiting to help. Their attention is riveted.

"In here"—she clutches the curtains behind her—"we have"—she crouches slightly, legs apart "an eighteen-year-old man"—now she stares hard and blinks—"with hemorrhoids. He's taken bowel softeners, but it hurts when he sits on something hard."

Alison is now sitting atop one of the steel tables. "Try to figure out if he's really followed his treatment. Tell him it's either surgery or sitting on a pillow."

Kirstin steps back into the cubicle. Her voice drifts over the curtain. "You can sit on a pillow." The residents titter.

She comes out again. "He has the smallest hemorrhoids I've ever felt and he doesn't blink at the rectal exam. He's been examined so many times, he's not embarrassed. Isn't he rather young for that type of problem?"

"It depends on what he's been doing," says Alison, laughing.

A chubby-cheeked young man in platform shoes and a fur-trimmed leather jacket walks out of the cubicle with a new piece of paper in his hand and firm instructions.

Now Carol Carse catches Alison's attention. She is seated next to a voluble, obese man whose inside jacket pockets are crammed with a surprising number of small disposable flashlights loaded with Pen-lite batteries.

"Where'd you get all those Pen-lites?" she asks.

"I sell 'em to my friends."

"Sell 'em? You *stole* them."

The man doesn't know what to say, but he is not offended. Carol talks to her patients in a half-kidding pointed way and spends considerable time establishing a rapport. ("Sometimes too long," says Alison, "when there is lab work to be done.") Carol is black, like 99 percent of the patients in this hospital encircled by a black ghetto.

Today after clinic there is time for a quick late lunch in the cafeteria. On the menu, dried meat loaf and soggy string beans. The food seems in keeping with the institution. As a last-minute idea, Alison invites the two female medical students, Kirstin and Julie, to join her.

They wait patiently in a long line holding stainless-steel trays and eyeing the bulletin-board menu.

"The boys are interested in you only as available date material," says Julie, commenting about her male colleagues' joshing. She wears not a trace of lipstick on a full mouth, and her long blonde hair is drawn tightly and unaffectedly behind her ears. "I was living with a guy outside of the medical school for the first two years, and I didn't know any of the men. I didn't have any men as friends because I was just not an available date. They'll go after the nurses even more because they're docile and trained to look up to the doctors. The doctors are the big heroes. When our group rotates through, the nurses will say 'Oh, no! Not another bunch of women doctors on this rotation.'

"There's a little bit of flirting, a little bit of a sexual message when a doctor gives an order to a nurse. The doctor winks at the nurses. Just let a woman wink at a doctor!"

Julie looks away briefly through the yellow-curtained windows. "The nurses know that doctors are good marriage material. They'll earn a good income and there'll always be work."

The tall, attractive Kirstin agrees. "A few male doctors marry women doctors," she reflects. "But the women doctors get married very, very slowly, and a lot less women than men get married.

"When I was a freshman med student, there was a guy, a sophomore, that I flirted with. We made eyes at each other and there was a sexual message. He would ask me to lunch and I got the impression that eventually he would want a lot more than lunch. Well, one day I was talking to one of the students and he said, 'Oh, have you met his wife? She's really nice.' I said, 'Oh, yeah, really nice.' Yikes! I felt surprised, disappointed, pissed off, and a little depressed. I might have been interested under the right circumstances, but the relationship never advanced and I didn't think it would be too cool. It was an 'I'm-going-to-play-around-with-the wife' game."

Kirstin shrugs. "I like to flirt and I like to feel I'm feminine as well as professional. That's how I like to seem and I don't think it reflects on my professional ability at all. But that isn't the image Julie wants to project."

Julie smiles slightly in agreement. She appears quietly womanly, in a plain, well-groomed way. She sighs as she picks up a styrofoam cup and presses the lever to the coffee-dispenser urn. "This is my favorite subject. I used to think about it and ask about it and fight about it all the time. 'What do you think of a woman in medicine?' 'I think it's all right as long as she's feminine.' 'What do you mean by feminine?' 'Oh, if she walks the right way. If she talks the right way.' Now I won't argue anymore. I've decided I have to protect my sanity.

"There's a girl in our class who would stand up in class and object to all these references, and she got quite a reputation as a women's libber. People started to give her a hard time, and now, when she walks into the room, her face seems to say 'Pick on me!' "

"And people *do*," adds Kirstin. "I actually once heard her say to one of the women faculty members, 'Do you think I can *really* be a woman and a professional too?' She seems to be riddled with self-doubt. Otherwise she's an athletic kind of girl and a real fighter. But she's never gotten back to that self-confidence she felt the first year. Now when she gets up in class, they'll shout; 'Shut up, Joan! Quiet, Joan!' "

Kirstin cocks her head to find a free table in a crowded room with a steadily swelling background chatter.

Weaving around several tables, they head toward one near the window.

Don Wilder and John Kirke approach the table carrying their lunch trays. ''Move over,'' Don tells Julie. Craig Armstrong, another first-year surgical resident, takes the end seat next to Alison, and Kirstin, who has momentarily gone to fetch some flatware, pulls up an extra yellow vinyl chair.

Wilder, a good-looking likable bachelor, eyes the women at the table. He smiles. His words are measured. His eyes flash with mischief. ''I think . . . that the place for women in medicine . . . is in *nursing*.'' Laughter. Wilder exposes a brilliant expanse of white teeth. He is teasingly goading the women, anticipating their reactions.

''No, really,'' Wilder insists more seriously, ignoring his food and thinking back to his days in medical school. ''I would look around at some of the girls in my class and I really wondered if something in their upbringing had made them masculine. I even went to the extreme of asking them out. But you know, they do have masculine traits. You ask them, 'What are you going into? Pediatrics?' And they say, 'Oh, no! Why are you always putting women in pediatrics?' '' Pause. ''It's the same thing when a man goes into hairdressing. I wonder about his masculinity.'' Pause. ''And usually I'm right.'' Big laughter. White teeth.

One striking and dynamic woman surgeon has said that it was not uncommon to hear in medical school, ''You don't look as if you should be a doctor.'' A surgeon was even more unthinkable. The image was one of an unattractive, aggressive female.

''Why did you ask out those women med students?'' asks Julie, sticking her neck out once again.

''The same reason why I ask out any woman.'' Loud laughter. White teeth.

''Why do you call it a masculine profession?'' wonders Kirstin.

''Because until very recently most of the doctors were men,'' says Wilder matter-of-factly.

''Why is that 'masculine'? Why don't you say 'male-dominated'?''

''I think women in medicine are great,'' offers John Kirke. ''I think there are specialties where they are more suited, though. Like pediatrics, because of their maternal instinct. I think children like a woman better than a man. OB-GYN too, because, even though you need stamina, there are a lot of women who would prefer to go to another woman. Surgery is more difficult because it's a male chauvinist pig specialty. You can just look at the head of the surgical program here and know he's a male chauvinist pig. He's so pompous.''

Some women in training in surgery have said that they would never publicly admit to feeling sick—having menstrual cramps, for instance—that such honesty might work against them. Some men, they say, expect women to be sickly, to complain about a headache, to have to lie down. In surgery, though, it's not really the thought that the blood and gore might upset women that puts men off, but the fear that the men will be stuck with extra work.

Alison has been listening and hurrying to finish her lunch. ''I would go absolutely crazy if I stayed home all day,'' she interjects. ''It would destroy me. I come to work every day because I like it. There's no reason in the world why I have to work, but I enjoy medicine and I want to help patients. My mother always complained bitterly that she only did housework, even though she had a master's in organic chemistry, which is more education than my father had.''

''I hate to say my mother is just a housewife, but that's what she is,'' Wilder says. ''*Just* a housewife. When my brother and I left''— he makes a long downward gesture with his thumb—''depression. She was really depressed. Nothing more for her to do. I want my wife to have a profession. I don't want to come home and talk about dirty diapers. I mean, I want to know about it but I want to talk about something else. I don't want a great brain because I'm not an intellectual giant myself, but I would like to marry a professional.''

Kirstin is confused. ''Why do you want your wife to have a profession? Because you want someone to talk to or so she won't go out of her mind?''

''When I get The Big One,'' says Wilder, holding both hands over his heart, ''she'll have to support herself. I'm certainly not the one to do it. We're going to spend every cent we've got.''

''When it came time in medical school for learning to do physical exams,'' recalls Kirstin, ''the girls went into one curtained room and the boys went into another. Some of us protested, and we had a group which volunteered to examine each other. It wasn't even a gynecological exam or a rectal exam, for God's sake. That you learn on a poor patient.''

"That poor woman," says Julie.

"We were looking at arms, legs, abdomen; there's nothing wrong with that. The only thing it would involve is being topless."

"Were you topless, Kirstin?" Wilder asks, grinning mischievously at her across the table.

"No! I never take my top off," says Kirstin emphatically, hugging her white coat around her chest. "I sleep with it. I take a shower and then I put my top back on." General amusement. Don Wilder smiles appreciatively at her.

"I close my eyes when I take a shower," he says, shutting his eyelids and patting his body. "I don't know if I have any marks on me."

Now Craig relaxes with a cigarette, puffing slowly. "The only time, the first time, I really ever got involved with a patient was with a twenty-four-year-old girl who was dying of liver cancer. One of her doctors had told her that she couldn't possibly have cancer of the liver. She was too young. There was something about her personality. I just couldn't sleep at night thinking about it."

"I remember her, too," says Alison, shaking her head emphatically. "Dorothy. I remember once driving home and my car radio started to play Rod McKuen's 'Seasons in the Sun.' 'Good-bye, my friend, it's time to die.' I started to cry and almost couldn't drive the car anymore."

"Even though she was already yellow and bloated," explains Craig, "you could tell she was a beautiful person."

"She was green," interjects Wilder. "I remember her. She had a beautiful set."

Julie's chin drops and she stares in wonder and disbelief. "I don't believe it," she says. "You are just terrible. Shut your mouth."

"The thing that surprised me most about this girl," Craig continues, "was that she was so composed, so cheery, so happy to see you. She had actually accepted this whole thing that she was going to die. She'd say, 'Come see. . . .' "

Wilder, interrupting: "Come up and see me sometime."

Julie, shocked: "You are just gross."

"Don is incorrigible," laughs Kirstin. "He calls me sweetie and I call him cutie just to get back at him."

Julie thinks intently for a moment, forgetting the remainder of her lunch. "Would you give good medical care to a woman who was ugly?" she asks.

"Women don't have to be beautiful," says Don, suddenly serious. "What they don't know is that they have to do very little to be attractive. They can just put on a certain dress and be attractive. I've really been turned on by a dress. Or eye makeup."

Julie is still groping for words as the group leaves the cafeteria to head back to the surgery floor.

"I would really resent having to spend two hours before I come to work just to paint myself up," she concludes, as the group of residents and medical students piles into the elevator to the second floor.

"Well said," smiles a man, probably a visitor, standing in the back of the elevator.

# 15
# Learning to Laugh All the Way

Today Alison Merrill and Mrs. Greer, the hospital caseworker, have collided in the gray semicircle which is the second-floor nurses' station. Mrs. Greer, well dressed and poised, listens with a steely mien, her arms folded across a thick stack of files.

"Can you arrange for visiting-nurse service or housekeeping for Loretta Rider?" Alison asks, or maybe demands.

Mrs. Greer tightens her jaw. The attractive, businesslike, no-nonsense woman in her middle thirties has an air about her which seems to say "Don't try to fool *me* or pull the wool over *my* eyes."

She looks intently at Alison through narrowed eyes; then opens and examines Loretta's file closely, looking at her address. "This is a section of old, detached houses. Big, *old* detached houses. Some of them frame. This indicates she is getting some form of public assistance because her income is below a certain level for this neighborhood." Mrs. Greer shakes her head. "She must be keeping boarders. They think if they tell you everything you won't help them. I let them say everything they want to say. Some will ask for a new suit or a $2,000 loan. Then I tell them where *I'm* coming from. Otherwise they'll try to manipulate you. I know *immediately* when I'm being manipulated."

Clutching her files, Mrs. Greer walks ramrod-straight down the hall toward Loretta's room.

"She's a tough lady," Alison comments, "but somehow she'll work it out so that Loretta will move out of an expensive $150-a-day hospital bed and into her house, comfortably and safely. Loretta won't need that day-to-day hospital and nursing care until near the end.

"You find yourself toughening up after a while. You see so many drunks come in with the same complaint. They'll yell at you and swing at you. Then the residents get clobbered by the social workers for becoming hardhearted with these drunks, especially the 'social dispositions,' the patients who have nowhere to go after they leave the hospital."

Hank Sanchez looks up from writing his orders. "Do you want to see a candidate for a euthanasia clinic? She's fifty-one and a cerebral palsy victim. She's all flexed up." Hank bends his wrists and freezes his hands under his chin. "She was admitted directly by the Home Care physician for treatment of her bedsores. All I'm doing is putting ointment on her. This is the first case I've had. It's no goddamn learning experience. She's impacted up to her eyeballs, which is probably why they are brown."

Dr. Sanchez winces at his own joke, then goes back to noting his orders on the chart.

Since she has missed breakfast again, Alison runs down the stairs toward the first-floor snack machines. As she hurries back toward the stairway exit, the loudspeaker's shrill tones blare in her ears. The message is as urgent as the voice is calm.

"Emergency Room. STAT. Emergency Room. STAT."

Jesus Christ.

STAT is short for the Latin *statim*, which means "immediately!" but in hospital code it means "emergency!" Alison has her own terse explanation. "There are two emergency codes," she cracks, " 'Code Blue,' which means the patient's croaking, and 'STAT,' which means he hasn't croaked yet but he's on the way. You often have a fine choice. You can either let your own patient wait on the operating room table or let somebody else's die in the Emergency Room."

Alison Merrill spins on her heels. She dodges past and in and out and around the people arriving at the hospital that morning, bursting into the Emergency Room at a full run and into a flurry of noisy activity.

"Does anyone have a unit of plasma ready to go?"

"May I have an amp of bicarb?"

"May I have one milligram of atropine?"

"I feel some rhythm."

A knot of people surround the motionless body of a man in cardiac arrest, shot in the chest by police during a robbery attempt. His legs are spread-eagled on the stretcher. He is abnormally quiet and pale.

"Oh, my God," says an annoyed E.R. nurse, peeved at the lack of elbow room as more and more physicians answer the STAT call. "People, people, people."

Alison feels over his chest with a stethoscope and listens. No breath sounds. The man is more dead than alive. A husky orderly next to her punches the lifeless chest violently up and down. The sheets are soaked with blood. The man—whoever he is—is "bleeding out." Probably massive internal injuries.

Another man, partially covered by a white sheet, snores obliviously on a stretcher parked and forgotten in a corner. Probably an overdose.

Nearby are two waiting policemen, bored and indifferent.

"Have you gotten a statement?" one asks the other routinely.

"No." He stares blankly at the inert body. "They just told me to get in the wagon and come here."

A nurse tries unsuccessfully to page another university's surgical service, which is taking admissions for the day. The residents must be in the O.R.

A medical resident wants a surgical resident to insert a chest tube in order to drain the chest cavity of blood and to equalize air pressure between the chest cavity and atmosphere, but Alison doesn't respond.

She has surgically placed a chest tube only once before. Yesterday, standing with Dave Fayard in a narrow supply room, surrounded by sterile gauze pads and oval eye pads, with the patient stretched out and moaning slightly on a wheeled bed in front of her.

"Push too hard with the tube and you can go right through the diaphragm (remember Bella Johnson?) and into the spleen, and then you have to take him to the O.R. Believe me, it's easy to do," Dave had admonished her.

Alison now decides against screwing up another university's patient.

Instead she asks for a needle and suture to anchor the I.V. securely into the skin. The intraveneous tubing will be used as a medication pipeline and is an essential emergency procedure. She has seen too many cases where the I.V. popped out when the chest was violently pumped in a last-ditch effort to resuscitate the patient.

Other medical personnel arrive to take over. Time to go.

Running out of the Emergency Room, Alison bumps against a young physician, smiling and dapper, who steadies his cup of steaming coffee. He grins broadly at Alison in greeting. "I would have come but I hadn't quite finished my coffee."

Alison half groans and runs off without really answering except by facial expression.

"That's one of my patients, I mean one of the doctors, Jake Pell, a neurosurgeon," says Alison of the man she almost doused with hot coffee. "A real character. I think he needs neurosurgery himself."

She races up the stairs and hurries to the operating room suites, where she is scheduled to assist in the repair of an epigastric hernia.

Soon scrubbed, gowned and gloved, she helps paint the patient's abdomen with brown antiseptic Betadine, then helps pat the abdomen dry with sterile towels.

Dave Fayard, normally deadpan, perks up with interest. He wants to tell the story he heard about another female surgical resident. "Do you know the one about the girl who slammed doors?" He turns to Alison.

"No," says Alison, her eyes shining with amusement as she spreads a sterile plastic sheet over the area of the incision. A small "window" in the sheet exposes only the surgical field. Draped and hidden from view, the body becomes gradually depersonalized, seems to disappear, an abstract figure in a medical landscape. A five-inch raised screen of drapes hides the patient's face from the surgical team.

"Well, for a few days this girl came in and slammed doors. You know, she was in a bad mood for several days. One of the residents was sure she was getting her period, and went through her purse one day to look for her birth control pills to figure out when her period was due."

Alison is still amused.

In a way, she enjoys her male colleagues' teasing.

One woman resident in surgery parries the gibes about her hormonal cycles by saying; "Don't bug me. It's that time of the month."

A resident going through her training describes a particular attending surgeon at her hospital who constantly makes jokes about women, and enjoys kidding all his associates in a sarcastic way. Once he told her he thought that women should be knocked up, at home, in the kitchen.

Fine, said the woman resident, that sounded like a lot more fun. If she wasn't in the O.R. to assist him the following day, it would be because she was being knocked up at home in the kitchen. She senses that if this surgeon were to see someone annoyed by his barbs, he would pick on them all the more. If he sees a well-endowed, good-looking female medical student, he asks her to "please assume The Position," which is to stand right next to him at the operating table.

But there was also the attending surgeon who asked permission of the female surgical resident before taking off his scrub pants, accidentally wringing wet with irrigation saline. She thought he was kidding, and the scrub nurse made no comment.

After finishing the case comfortably dressed the surgeon walked casually out of the O.R., exposing a pair of light blue shorts through the slit in his hospital gown. The scrub nurse looked shocked. The surgical resident's amused comment was that at least the shorts were clean.

"You've opened and closed, opened and closed a thousand times," Alison reflects. "You discover that if you spent the whole time in the O.R. being serious, you would go crazy."

A hole has worn through the elbow of her white coat.

The day-to-day routineness of the residents' hospital work helps promote a certain irreverence—or so it would seem to an outsider—with which the human body is handled. After a while, death and trauma are no less a surprise than a coffee break.

In the recovery room—that place of pulsating monitors and bleeping noises and postoperative crises—Alison spies Wilson Lane, a surgical resident she hasn't seen around the hospital for a while. He is bent over an old wizened woman curled up in pain. It is just another operating day, and neither one seems to notice her shrieks of pain.

"We spent one week in the Caribbean," he tells Alison.

"Ooooh, ooooh, ooooh," wails the woman.

"Oh, that's so great!" bursts Alison with enthusiasm.

"OOOOOH, OOOOH, OOOOH."

". . . I'm so jealous."

"Yes, we went from Saturday to Saturday," Wilson Lane explains.

Then he bends down toward the patient. "You'll be O.K., Mrs. Lester. There was a little tumor on your lung. We took that out. We took out part of your lung."

As Alison leaves the floor that evening to drive home at last, she passes 201 South, where an R.T. has been called—the cardiac resuscitation team. Five people are clustered in the room, some in scrubs, some in white coats.

A sixty-year-old white-haired woman with a distended stomach and pendulous breasts lies on one of the two beds with her head flung back and her mouth stretched wide. A purse is thrown over the bed. A bowl of fruit rests on the windowsill, some letters, some Kleenex.

Alison tunes into the conversation and watches briefly at the doorway while someone violently thumps the stricken woman's chest, up, down, up, down.

The portable EKG's screen shows a flat line, and is curiously noiseless.

"Hey, is this plugged in?"

Another EKG from 2 North has just been rolled over and is plugged into the wall.

"How long was she out before she was found?"

"Just a few minutes."

"Must be. She's still as warm as hell."

A nurse peers at the moving outlines on the EKG monitor screen. "It's called dying heart. I keep telling you. We're losing voltage rapidly here." She laughs.

Someone turns off the TV.

Tonight Alison Merrill is not too tired to be pensive. "This is my fifth year in medicine," Alison says slowly sorting her thoughts, "and I've decided it's a terrible thing to get involved on too much of a personal basis with a patient. The few times that I've seen nurses, or occasionally a doctor, or even myself get a little more involved, for whatever reason, it becomes a little more difficult to cope with what's happening, with a complication, with death. You'll hear people joking about a dying patient's underwear. I would think it would be frightening for lay people to see our reactions to certain things. Our superficial levity is just something to break up the tension, something to help us cope with the multiple times we see death, trauma, blood, and gore.''

The emergency in the E.R. that morning didn't make it. His liver was lacerated by a .38-caliber bullet.

# 16
# Life Outside the Hospital: "He Uses Johnson's Paste Wax and I Use Mop & Glo"

As Mike hunches over his desk, bending over his books for a nighttime community college management course, Alison sidles over to him and presses her body snugly against his. She places her head on top of his and starts to play with his ear.

He sighs. "I don't think I could stand having you around all the time," he complains with mock annoyance. "I wouldn't get anything done."

Some nights Alison just comes home and falls asleep. Mike wakes her up long enough to see if she wants any scrambled eggs before she falls back into a torpor. The proliferating neon shopping centers in their area are dotted with little ethnic restaurants, and sometimes they will go out to dinner to save the bother of cooking and cleaning up. Mike doesn't mind making his own sandwich as long as he doesn't have to cook for the two of them when she is home.

When Mike works the 3:30-to-midnight shift at the plant, she "waits up" for him after the fashion of tired surgical residents who catch up on their sleep at every opportunity—asleep on the living room couch so he can wake her when he arrives home.

At the office Mike will occasionally talk about this broad who shows up once or twice a week, opens the door and says "Hi, I'm home," stays around for a couple of hours too tired to talk, and then disappears for a few days.

His traditional-husband friends see their wives' role as staying at home with their children, pressing their clothes, and cooking. Mike tells them to eat their hearts out. When he has a $100,000 house, he'll invite them all over.

"Of course," Mike says, "this life is not for everyone." He is not interested in building a social life. His clothes aren't always pressed, but they're clean. Eighty percent of the time his dinner is not cooked when he comes home. (Seventy-five percent of the time, Alison claims.)

Alison feels guilty if she comes home, props up her feet, and relaxes with the evening paper and a martini. There is always housework to be done or surgical journals to be read. The dishes tend to pile up in the sink, but since they own very few dishes anyway, the kitchen never looks irritatingly disorderly.

Weather permitting, they can play tennis on the courts directly behind their apartment dwelling. There is no fee and the courts are available to all of the residents. "But when I come home, I'm pretty much of a lump," she says, "and I don't make a very good tennis partner."

At Christmastime, Alison and Mike attend the surgery department's annual party, held at one of the big hotels in town, complete with waiters serving dinner and a live band.

Most of the men are wearing tuxedos, but Mike refuses to, telling Alison that her colleagues will have to accept him in a suit. At the dance, he feels awkwardly uncomfortable. The social chatter is nothing but medical chitchat. The subject might change for ten minutes or so, but then the conversation turns back to medicine. The residents and surgical staff are polite to Mike with a reserved friendliness. They don't essentially care about him because he cannot really help them get ahead. Their wives seem fairly well trained to sit and listen to their husbands.

It strikes Mike that the university surgical staff considers itself "really special" and "high on the shelf." He finds he has to listen politely to the older professors' stories of how they got started. Dr. Shelton, the emeritus department head, tells him, chuckling at the tale, that his first patient was the dog of some rich person in the city; that was how his lucrative practice began.

At 12:15 A.M. the band stops playing, the dance is over, and Mike wants to go home. He doesn't want to listen to more stories. He doesn't particularly care if these people like him or not.

The next week they leave for a week's skiing in the Vermont hills. They rent a condominium for five days at Killington, and it rains four out of the five days. That is the last time, Alison tells Mike, that they will rent a condominium for a *vacation*. Mike can't understand when it is so much cheaper than a hotel room. But Alison complains that she will be damned if she'll ever cook and clean on a vacation again.

Mike bowls with friends at least once a week in winter when she is on duty. It is too expensive to play more often than that. Occasionally they will bowl together, although Mike is a much more skillful player than she. "He's upset even when he gives me a head start and I manage to beat him because he's spotted me 100 points."

Sometimes Alison will invite some of her hospital colleagues for dinner. They will drink a few beers and sip wine with the meal.

On one occasion Alison goes to the trouble of preparing a multi-course dinner for a few of the residents with their wives and girlfriends. While Mike is busy talking on the other side of the living room, Alison is asked why she uses her married name.

Alison is silent for a moment. "There was no real purpose for me to keep my maiden name," she explains. "We aren't in the same profession. He's in electronics and I'm in medicine, and we're not going to publish in the same journals. And I could see us socially at a cocktail party where he would be meeting the house staff and people wouldn't know what to call him." She pauses. "And even though he didn't say much about it, I could tell that when we were married he would be hurt if I didn't take his name."

"You have to think of that fragile male ego, don't you," says one surgical colleague who used to be married to a woman physician and is now divorced.

A few months before the wedding, Alison had gone to pick up the spanking-new doctor's bag which one of the big drug companies was offering the graduating senior medical students as a gift. It was the classic little black leather bag with her name stamped in gold. ALISON SAUNDERS, M.D. Graduation was still three or four months away, and it was the first time she felt that she was really going to make it.

When she displayed the bag proudly to Mike, he interrupted her flow of excitement. ''Oh,'' he said, ''that isn't the right name.'' He sounded disappointed.

Whether or not to use her married name was not something the couple discussed formally, weighing the pros and cons in a rational manner. It was something Alison decided herself through the inner perceptions of her being, finding the spiritual glue which unites two people.

Her biweekly paycheck, made out to Alison Merrill, M.D., arrives directly in their apartment mail. Mike deposits the check into a joint account, converting a certain amount into pocket cash and storing the reserve money in his jewelry box on top of his bedroom dresser. Alison takes whatever she needs for her car, gas, and mealtime expenses at the hospital. Mike pools his own salary with her paycheck and pays all the bills. At the moment they are saving to fulfill the American Dream and buy a single-family home.

''I can get along perfectly well without her as far as wifely duties go,'' he will say to friends, teasing Alison to her face. ''Frankly, I couldn't stand someone ironing my underwear all the time, and I'm away as much as she is. I just want her to be there when I'm home, and I tell her I want her to go out and make lots of money. . . . After all, it's not the same thing as putting her on the street.''

But Alison's precious leisure time frequently does *not* coincide with Mike's. The hardest adjustment for Mike—and what surely riles him the most—is her inability to meet a predictable schedule. She is often not available when he is counting on her to be available.

Estimating when she will be able to go off duty, she will hurriedly call him from the hospital during a lull: ''I'll meet you in half an hour in front of the hospital—O.K., Mike?'' He has now accustomed himself to automatically waiting an extra half hour in the car.

Or she will call and say; ''I'll be home in an hour. Put the potatoes in, O.K.?'' He won't do it anymore until she gets there. He has found that her chances of coming home when she says she will are close to zero.

Alison handles the situation by putting very few limits on how Mike spends his free time without her. "Mike leads very much the bachelor life he had before we were married—going out with the guys for a few beers, for instance. He accepts my life in a strange way in that he considers me his roommate"—she laughs—"in many respects. It sounds less final."

Mike will come up to the kitchen stove on a Sunday afternoon, grinning wryly, his hands on his hips.

"Alison?"

"Yes, Mike?"

"Is the corn burning?"

"I don't think so but I'll check."

Alison lifts the aluminum pot lid, checks the overly generous amount of bubbling liquid, stirs the mixture with a wooden spoon, and turns down the gas flame ever so slightly. She adds an extra quantity of water. Recently she did burn the corn, discovering her oversight only by the faintly putrid smell which began to fill the apartment.

"My roommate," Mike says mistrustfully but pleasantly, "has a habit of leaving on the stove, the gas, the electricity, everything."

Mike has an "I told you so" air about him as if he truly expected a conflagration in the kitchen although nothing was amiss—as if catastrophe is possible unless he is careful to check up on her.

"Mike thinks there are only three kinds of vegetables," Alison mutters as he leaves the kitchen. "Corn on the cob, creamed corn, and whole-kernel corn."

To most spouses, doctors don't look like heroes for very long.

Alison is forced to concentrate and marshal her energies for her professional rather than her home life. At the hearth, ironically, she seems like a hapless woman playing house. Physically unassuming ("She cuddles snugly right under my arm," Mike will say in one of his teasing moods), her total impression is not overpowering, which is probably why the marriage works.

The kitchen, with its yellow and green plaid wallpaper, is cheery. A red rug and a bright modern painting by an unknown California artist light up the living room. A snow-filled Colorado ski poster is taped to the bathroom door. The dark-wooded coffee table supports several scattered issues of *Annals of Surgery,* a monthly review. The apartment makes no effort to be pretentious, just comfortable.

"We tell our friends," says Alison, " 'Come up and see us sometime.' And when they do, we can just throw the newspapers in the closet and the place looks neat. What do we do about the housework in the apartment? Not an awful lot." She laughs.

Alison has adjusted by changing her attitude toward housekeeping. She has adopted her mother-in-law's philosophy, which runs something like "If-my-friends-don't-like-the-way-I-keep-house-then-they-don't-have-to-come-see-me." Her mother-in-law is not the best cook nor the best housekeeper, but in her home there is always room for an extra last-minute guest and always enough food.

A small, rotund woman, mother Merrill is one of those housewifely women who will do anything for her children; she wants to feel that her children still need her.

When she comes to visit, she is apt to say anxiously to her 5'11" son, "Are you still eating one hot meal a day, Mike?"

"She stopped," claims Alison, "when I said, 'Yeah, I give him at least one hot hamburger a day.' "

Alison's mother, on the other hand, is a meticulous housekeeper. When a visitor arrives, Mrs. Saunders is horrified if her house is not immaculate. Consequently Alison didn't bring people home from school very often; it was just too much of a hassle to call at least three hours in advance and then hear her mother complain.

Alison's parents both graduated from pharmacy school but only briefly practiced together in their hometown drugstore. Alison's father never cleaned up after filling a prescription, which annoyed Alison's mother. She would carefully plug the pharmaceutical bottles and shelve them properly, which annoyed Alison's father. So after a short time, Alison's mother decided to give up her practice; yet she complained bitterly when her essential job became housework. That was not her idea of what she was meant to do.

Years ago, Alison can remember not being able to see Mike on a weekend morning because he had to help his mother wax the kitchen floor. With a husband frequently away from home, and with four rambunctious boys and no daughters, Mike's mother had to turn to her sons for household help.

Now Mike helps Alison shine their own kitchen floor. Occasionally when the film becomes discolored and gritty, he will strip the floor and rewax it for her. He uses Johnson's Paste Wax and she uses Beacon's Mop & Glo.

"In the beginning," says Alison, "I felt I had to do right by him and cook him a big dinner when I got home. Chicken Kiev from *The Joy of Cooking* was a favorite. Now he can't understand why I just throw a breast of chicken into the oven. If he wants Chicken Kiev, he has to pound the chicken breasts thin and flat with a wooden mallet. Over the year I've come to simplify meals. Luncheon-meat sandwiches or we just go out for pizza. I leave bacon and eggs for an evening meal when I don't feel like cooking.

"I think," laughs Alison good-naturedly, "that my neighbors rationally acknowledge that I go to the hospital every day and go to work, but they cannot rationally picture me as a physician or a surgeon. Particularly with some of the boners that I've pulled. They think it is a Big Joke. Maybe it is."

At times, Alison will receive an urgent, nighttime call from one of her suburban neighbors—like the one from Sally White.

Sally and Gregg are a few years older than Alison and Mike, live in the apartment directly under theirs, and are one of the few couples with whom Alison and Mike socialize in their housing development. Usually there isn't enough time to do much neighborly socializing.

Now, Sally knows perfectly well that Alison knows absolutely nothing about pediatrics—at least Alison thinks she should. But Alison finds herself pulled into helping a distressed neighbor anyway.

"Alison," says Sally breathlessly into the phone. "Chris has a rash! I don't know if it's the measles or not. Come down and see it!"

"How do *I* know if it's the measles or not?" Alison exclaims truthfully. "The only pediatrics I ever did was in the hospital, and they don't bring kids to the hospital for measles. I've never seen a case of measles in my life!"

"Well, don't you have any books?"

"O.K. I'll go see if I can find something." Since Alison worked as a part-time librarian during medical school to meet her expenses, she simply checked out most necessary medical tomes in order to save money. She doesn't even own her own pediatrics textbook.

However, she takes out her trusted DeGowin and DeGowin *Bedside Diagnostic Examination,* looks up a verbal description of the measles, and totes the volume downstairs to Sally's apartment.

"Well," Alison announces, "this is the description for measles, and this is the description for chicken pox. I don't know. It really doesn't look like either one, but it looks more like chicken pox than measles.''

After both puzzled women study the restless, uncomfortable, five-year-old child, Alison suggests, straight-faced; ''If you really want to know, why don't you take him to the doctor's tomorrow and find out?''

The family pediatrician takes one look at the child and diagnoses roseola, with an aside to Sally that Alison should stick to her surgery because she surely doesn't know anything about pediatrics.

# 17
# Male and Female Patients

Mike doesn't fret that some of the men in the fast-paced hospital environment might make advances to his wife.

"Don't worry," Alison tells Mike, not taking any incident very seriously. "I can take care of myself."

During medical school, a hospital administrator the age of her father once made a pass which she rebuffed. She was keeping a dog illegally in her hospital room at the time and the next day she received a note from the administration that she had twenty-four hours to get the dog *out.* An X-ray technician cornered her in the darkened X-ray developing lab and asked how tall her husband was. She exaggerated a little. A male scrub tech—the person who hands a surgeon the instruments—who was 6'4'' tall and weighed 270 pounds suggested they get together after hours and she laughingly answered that her husband wouldn't like that very much.

"So what," he replied.

"He's bigger than you are," she retorted, smiling at the outrageous comparison.

Mike worries more about her safety coming home alone at night from City Hospital, walking through an emptied parking lot, stopping her car at red lights along deserted streets.

Hospital work and its occasional sexual overtones are a favorite, continuing subject among residents. On one of the few evenings when they meet together socially, they enjoy exchanging lighthearted experiences while sipping red and white wines and nibbling on crackers with onion or clam dip. It is a special gathering for Kirstin's twenty-fourth birthday at her nearby apartment, and Alison has taken time off from her on-call nighttime schedule to come.

Craig Armstrong, shy, quiet, conscientious, claims he was assigned to examine a Voluptuous Blonde. He is vague about her malady but precise about her physical attributes. Noticing she wore a bra under her nightgown, he summoned up his best authoritative professional manner and commanded, "Would you mind taking off your breasts so I can examine your bra?" Even more flustered by his verbal confusion, he spun around to leave the room, knocking her bedpan from the bed to the floor with a jarring clatter.

Later he tells of working in the suture section of the Emergency Room when a nurse came in, grinning broadly, holding up a prospective patient's chart with the tips of her well-manicured fingers.

"I have here," the nurse said as disinterestedly as possible, "a twenty-two-year-old stewardess-hostess." The waiting girl had something minor, like a slight cut on her hand. Craig and another resident raced across the room, colliding in the doorway. Somehow the other resident got to the girl first. "He disappeared behind the gray curtain of the treatment room," smiles Craig, "ordered X-rays, everything, and spent three hours talking with her."

"It always helps to be young and attractive no matter what you do," reflects Alison later.

Kirstin Fernie, their hostess, a conscientious medical student, contributes a story about an embarrassing neurological exam. The male patient's history mentioned some psychiatric symptoms. His chart also noted he was a minister and sketched a long-standing injury to his spinal column, with some possible symptoms of a tumor. Kirstin slid the curtain around its ceiling track to close off the patient's bed, and as part of a complete neurological work-up, she tested for the cremasteric reflex: If, when she stimulated the skin of the front and inner side of the thigh, the testis retracted on the same side, she could ascertain the soundness of the cord between the first and second lumbar nerves. After all, wasn't that what the textbook said to do?

The patient responded with an erection and began to get fresh.

"I blushed deep red," says Kirstin, "took his hands off my breasts, and put them on his head. His wife was sitting patiently on the other side of the curtain and I couldn't say a thing. He started to whisper that he slept with his wife but that wasn't enough, so he masturbated.''

One of the illogics of hospital procedure is that a female nurse cannot catheterize a male patient, but a doctor can, which sometimes means that Alison is paged by the floor nurse.

"Nurses can clean the male patients when they crap all over the place," Alison grumbles. "No doctor would want to do that, but no hospital that I know of will let a female nurse catheterize a man. That's supposed to be a doctor's job.''

"The first time it happened I asked the nurse, 'How come you can't do it?'

"She said, 'Because I'm not allowed to.'

"I said, 'Well, I'm a woman and you're a woman; why can't you do it?'

"She said, 'Well, those are the rules.'

"Then I told her that I had never done it and I had absolutely no idea how to do it. Could she teach me?

"She said, 'Sure.' So she, the nurse, ended up showing me what to do.

"It gives you an idea how petty hospitals can be. Catheterizing a man can be more of a problem than catheterizing a woman. The male urethra is longer, with more possibility of a stricture or obstruction. You shouldn't push the catheter because it can traumatize the tissue. But logically, if the procedure is too tricky for a nurse, then male nurses shouldn't be allowed to catheterize a man either, which they are.

"In some hospitals they are trying to change this rule because the nurses get very upset at having to call somebody in the middle of the night to catheterize one of their male patients. Needless to say, the nurses get a lot of flack when they wake a resident at 3:00 in the morning. The residents are trying to get some sleep and the nurses are up anyway. That's their shift. And the nurses don't see any particular problem with it, especially if the resident is tied up doing something else.''

One of the old arguments against women doctors has been that since sexual excitability is physically more easily apparent in a man, men would be too embarrassed to consult them. This still holds true in urology, and only a handful of women physicians in the U.S.A. pursue this field as their medical specialty.

"I think it would be an even more difficult field than surgery for a woman to get patients,'' comments Alison realistically. ''I know that when at first I examined a guy for a hernia and he had an erection, he was embarrassed as hell and I was embarrassed. I used to have more difficulty examining men my own age. But I've decided that if you're at all flustered, it flusters him. Now I totally ignore the whole thing. I can't imagine that acknowledging it would make the situation any better.''

Alison returns from the party to the hospital at 10:00 P.M. The area is dark, with just a twinkling of streetlights along the driveway to the hospital. Up on the surgical floor, as she hangs up her coat and slips her white jacket back on over an emerald-green shirt paired with black wool slacks, she hears her name being called over the hospital loudspeaker. An unshaven, graying quasi-derelict in his late sixties has arrived at the Emergency Room, and Alison is being paged downstairs.

In a small treatment room radiating off the E.R., the querulous man hears her ask him to undress and put on a hospital gown, feels her fingers examining his abdomen for a hernia, watches her put on a rubber glove, and listens to her ask him to turn over on his left side. ''What the old guy basically saw,'' recounts Alison, ''was this young girl who was going to stick her fingers up his ass.''

''You're not going to do that to me,'' he objects.

''Well, why not?'' she counters. ''We just have to do it.'' He has rectal bleeding, and this exam is relatively important because of the omnipresent possibility of prostatic and certain kinds of rectal cancer.

''Well, you're just not going to do it to me.''

''I'm a doctor,'' she explains sternly.

''Yes?''

''I've got to examine you to decide what's wrong, or else we can't help you.''

''Well, you're not going to do that to me.''

''Then you really don't think that I'm a competent doctor?''

''Oh, yes, honey. Yes, you are,'' the man blubbers.

''You really make me feel awful, as if you don't trust me as a doctor.''

''Yeah, you're all right, but you're just not going to do that to me.''

''I can't take care of you if I can't examine you.''

The old man slowly and reluctantly gives in, with Alison continuing to prod him to make him feel bad for not trusting her. "People are reluctant enough about rectal exams without having some woman doing it," Alison laughs later with another resident at the nurses' desk which is the focal center of the Emergency Room. "I once told a graying, fifty-five-year-old company executive to roll over on his left side so I could do a rectal exam to check his prostate. He said squeamishly, 'I've never had this done before by a woman. I just have to keep in mind that you're a doctor!' What blows my mind is when a middle-aged woman asks, 'Are you an intern or a real doctor?' The standard joke is to send in the medical students."

Sometimes a woman will refuse a pelvic exam. One little old lady is eighty-nine, has never had a pelvic exam, and is not about to start now. Another woman has arrived to have her gallbladder removed and doesn't see how a pelvic exam as part of her routine physical upon admission can possibly be helpful, especially since she underwent a pelvic exam from her gynecologist a few months before.

A fifteen-year-old girl doubled over with abdominal pain has arrived with her mother. The girl looks older than her years but seems frightened and unsure. Her mother hovers in the background talking to the nurses.

One of the standard examining questions for a girl with abdominal pain is; "Have you had intercourse?"

"Very early in the year I scratched that question," says Alison, "since it has a moral implication. It seems especially moralistic to a young, unmarried girl. There are a certain number of young girls who are brought up in a social ethic which says that they shouldn't have intercourse without wedlock, and if they feel that they are being discriminated against morally, then they are going to lie. Particularly if they want you to like them so that you will take good care of them, they will tell you what they think you want to hear. The really important thing to establish is whether they are sexually active and if they have had a recent sexual contact."

Alison must determine whether the girl has inflamed tubes and gonorrhea, as opposed to appendicitis. Now she asks; "When was the *last* time you had intercourse?"

The girl denies any sexual activity.

A short while later, writing up the girl's history at an available desk, Alison is reflective. "The type of rationale that is really hard for me to understand is the response when you ask, 'Are you interested in birth control?' 'No.' 'Well, do you want to get pregnant?' 'No.' ''

She sinks her back against the chair. ''As a woman surgeon maybe people might expect me to be more sympathetic than a male surgeon to a woman patient. But I think I am even less sympathetic to a neurotic woman complaining about everything—the type who goes to bed with a headache—because I think she typifies everything that men think is wrong with women. I am more tolerant of a neurotic man and I am much less sympathetic to women who are destroying the reputation of womankind.''

# 18
# Talking with Patients, Family, and Friends

An unsmiling young woman wants to talk to Alison privately during afternoon visiting hours. It is Sam Ferguson's girlfriend.

"You seem to be in charge here," she says to Alison, accosting her in the hall. "Can we talk? Sam Ferguson and I are planning to get married." They move to the drab conference room next to the nurses' station and sit down at the scratched wooden arm-desks.

About twenty-five years old, her hair tied back with a red kerchief, she wears a light wool dress over a plump, full figure. Peering intently at Alison, she appears calm, concerned, and sweet.

"We still don't know whether the spinal cord was really severed," Alison tells her. Jake Pell, the staff neurologist, thinks it was, but Alison doesn't say so. She is reluctant to upset this concerned woman with a medical opinion until the laboratory investigation is finished. Doctors generally don't discuss *all* the possibilities with the patients and their families, who are allowed to perceive only the tip of the medical iceberg.

Alison tells her the same thing over and over again. The woman nods her head up and down, soaking up all the information she can glean.

Again Alison repeats, "How much damage there is we're still trying to find out."

The woman seems reluctant to stop talking to Alison. Their chairs are pulled opposite each other and they talk quietly, face to face. The woman—she has never actually introduced herself by name—clutches her purse to her side, holds one finger to her mouth, and peers hard into Alison's eyes. Alison looks back curiously.

"We're thinking of getting married as soon as possible," says the young woman softly. "Is there any way of knowing what will happen? When he will recover?"

"There's *no* way," Alison emphasizes. "We just have to wait and see. Either he will get better or he won't—I have to tell you that. It might take weeks or months before we will know for sure. Pain would be the first sensation to come back. Then some other sensation."

Finally the woman seems satisfied that she knows all there is to know about Ferguson's condition. She sighs and stands up, preparing to leave. "Thank you very much. I just wanted to know where he stood as of now."

"That may set you back a little bit."

"So whenever I get the urge I can talk to you?"

"Sure you can," Alison says soothingly.

The woman turns and walks down to the far end of the corridor to a surgical male ward. Sam Ferguson is waiting anxiously for her, his head turned, studying the door from his bed in the far-right corner of the large, rectangular room.

"Is that Mr. Foster?" Alison says angrily, going into the hall. "I'll bop him over the head." Wearing pajamas and a bathrobe, Foster is wheeling himself to one of the pay phones, pushing the wheels hard with both hands. His foot, or rather the stump, is down, dangling over the edge of the footrest.

"You sure are a talkative guy."

"I get lonely here," he says, sorting the change in his hand.

"You need to keep your foot up," she orders. "Keep your foot up."

Foster has a poor blood supply to his extremities because of his diabetic condition. If the stump is not well vascularized, the area may swell, cutting off more blood, impeding healing, and potentially promoting infection. Then Alison would have to consider the next level of amputation.

"Keep your foot in an upward position," she scolds once again, waiting to see him lift his stump onto the footrest before walking to the nurses' station on the same floor.

Using one of the black phones at the nurses' station, Alison calls the hospital security police. She tells them that Sam Ferguson's family has received phone calls threatening his life.

"I told him not to mess with that woman," Ferguson's mother chided during a warning phone call to Alison this morning. "I told him not to mess with her."

The official police record still reads "unknown assailant," but Ferguson told Alison that the jilted father of his girlfriend's four-year-old son was the person who aimed the gun to his gut and made applesauce of his abdomen. He says he is coming into the hospital to finish the job. Ferguson mentioned that the same assailant shot a previous boyfriend over the same woman and left him paralyzed.

"The problem is," says Alison emphatically into the phone, "that I have to protect the nurses."

"It's the responsibility of the nursing staff to restrict visitors," says the man at the end of the line.

"Listen," Alison protests, "I'm all alone at night and you don't seriously think that either myself or the nurses will stand in the way of a man with a gun?"

"Basically you're just worried about Dr. Merrill."

"You're damn right I'm worried about Dr. Merrill!"

The upshot of the conversation is that the police will not put Ferguson in protective custody because their office receives too many calls which are empty threats. Essentially they will move in only when the first bullet is fired.

Alison hangs up, disgusted. "Often these people who come in like so much human wreckage won't even give any names because they want to go right back out and get even themselves. Or else it's a *friend* or a wife. And they're still friends when they leave. 'Oh, he didn't mean it.' She sighs. "I don't believe this. A man could walk in with a .45 in his hand and the nurses are supposed to say, 'Pardon me, you shouldn't do that.' "

She goes to seek out the unit's head nurse to warn her of the threats to Ferguson's life. "Those poor nurses will be the first line of defense."

Walking back into the hall toward the patients' rooms, she stops to see Loretta Rider, who is destined to go home soon to wait for death. Alison wants to ascertain—not being sure to what degree Loretta knows of or acknowledges her impending death—that she will have help at home.

Although there is a chair, Alison sits down close to Loretta on her bed, speaking softly in a room where there are three other patients.

"I don't mind being alone," says Loretta, who is composed.

"I mind, because you've just had a big operation. You're going to find out you're tired."

"There's nobody there. If I'm tired, I'll sit down or lie down. The only thing is I might go back to not eating good. I know it's not right, but I do it." Loretta stops to think for a moment.

Across the room in another bed, Rebecca Hanley heaves a long, inward sigh.

"EEEEEEEEEEEEEEEEEEEEEE!"

Alison glances across the room. A glassy-eyed, twisted form with straggly white hair drops an oversized baby blue rubber pretzel—probably a child's teething ring—which she was clutching with both hands. She grips her bed rail, her wrists bent at crazy angles. For fifty-one years she has slurped liquids from a baby bottle while her mother drizzled and slushed mushy foods day after day down her throat. Her bedsores are huge holes worn into her flesh, and the gleaming white hip joint is visible several inches down. A stultified brain in a dysfunctional body, Rebecca Hanley is nearly sightless, almost speechless. She has never talked, she has never walked.

A nurse steps into the room to decipher Rebecca Hanley's screech. "She cries a lot for her mother." Uttering a primal wail, her voice is an animal bleat.

The nurse picks up a baby bottle half-filled with orange juice which is lying in the bed. "Oh, good. She took a little of her bottle today."

Alison turns away to continue her painful scene with Loretta. "You have to start thinking of the future as far as tiredness and weakness are concerned."

"I don't anticipate any problems."

"We want to do what you want to do." Alison is softer, more measured, more sweet-voiced than usual.

"My son said that he was going to talk things over tonight. Maybe he'll talk to my brother. My son only has an efficiency, so that wouldn't be too good, I think."

"We'd like to have you around, but when you go home we'd like to think you're O.K."

Loretta starts to cry quietly, takes a tissue out of her pocket, and lifts her glasses to dab her eyes.

"To have somebody with you is probably the best thing to do. You have cancer and we want to know that you are being taken care of."

"I remember. You told me."

Alison strokes Loretta's arm gently.

"I just don't want to lie down and cry all the time. I think I want to be alone now before my son comes in . . . thank you."

On her way back to the nurses' station, Alison catches a glimpse of Ferguson's girlfriend through the doorway of his room. She is bending over his bed, her face close to her man's.

"The question is," Alison wonders out loud, "did she ditch her last boyfriend *after* he was paralyzed?" Her eyes sparkle shrewdly.

"Dr. Merrill?" Mrs. Sanders, the efficient head nurse, is calling Alison. "May I show you something?" Val Sanders is holding a metal pan. Mrs. Parks, one of Alison's patients, is vomiting and the brown vomit is suspicious.

Alison leaves the nurses' station and hurries down the hall. As she enters the four-bed room, Mrs. Parks is vomiting fecal-looking matter. There are brown splotches all over the sheets. The three other patients in the room stare dully from their chairs. Mrs. Parks retches and retches with low guttural sounds. The smell of feces surrounds the bed and the room.

"Easy now," says Alison.

How can she keep from throwing up herself?

As Alison hurries to push a nasogastric tube down a nostril, the espohagus, and into the stomach, brown liquid surges up both into the tube and out Mrs. Parks's mouth.

Vile. Vile. Vile. Alison has to turn her head away to keep from gagging. Endless quantity. The other patients notice that Alison's face looks queasy, and perk up with interest. They ignore Mrs. Parks. Mrs. Parks is soaked and shaking.

Later, Alison admits that three times she had to keep from vomiting herself. Sickening smells are much worse than operating room gore.

"Get me a suction pump," Alison tells Val Sanders.

"Have you had a bowel movement in a few days?" she asks Mrs. Parks. "When was the last time you passed gas and had a bowel movement?"

Could the problem be intestinal obstruction? The patient was admitted for biliary colic, that is, pain from the gallbladder.

Over a year ago, Mrs. Parks underwent a hysterectomy. Could there be an obstruction caused by adhesions from previous surgery? A physician has to weigh all the medical angles in what is called a differential diagnosis. The possibilities race through Alison's mind. Sitting blankly in her bed two days ago, reading an ''Amazing Spider-man'' comic book, mother of eleven children all admitedly born out of wedlock, the portly Mrs. Parks as she calls herself, had seemed impassive. But Alison sensed that there was a lot going through her mind. Something she said made Alison think she was scared she might be dying.

Mrs. Parks has vomited 2,500 cc. of fecal-looking material, not counting what has inundated her sheets.

Val Sanders calls to get a STAT X-ray in fifteen minutes.

Alison bumps into Dave in the hall. Fayard is always laconic and composed. ''Oh, yeah,'' he says. ''The X-ray last night showed a small bowel obstruction.'' Jesus Christ. Why didn't he tell her yesterday? Or this morning? Without X-ray verification, a clinical diagnosis of intestinal obstruction just didn't seem to make much sense.

While waiting for a new set of X-rays on Mrs. Parks, Alison completes her orders for the day on her patients' charts.

A hospital operator is paging Dr. Merrill. She picks up the phone. It is her husband. When will she be home, Mike asks? Will she be home to cook him dinner or should he make himself a sandwich?

Doesn't he remember that she is on call tonight? She still has several patient charts to complete. Then she will check on Mrs. Parks down at X-ray, down in the subterranean labyrinth of the hospital, to make sure that the woman will be processed quickly. When the X-ray results come back, Bernie Schmidt might decide to operate immediately. She'll have to call back. Mike sounds slightly petulant, and more resigned than accepting. ''Well, when will you be home tomorrow?'' he asks.

She offers an approximate time and laughs, pointing out that it might be four or five hours from then.

''Try to come home at a decent time,'' he tells her, feeling bad that she has to stay up so many long hours.

Her own good humor starts to ebb. She spends so much time walking around the hospital trying to get X-rays done that someone outside of X-ray asked her; ''Are you a radiologist?'' When she asked Bernie Schmidt if he wanted Mrs. Parks prepped for the O.R. and her blood typed and cross-matched, he said not to bother. Three hours from now, after the X-rays are developed, Bernie just might say, ''Let's take her to the O.R. I want that blood in half an hour.'' She'll tell him then that she asked him a while back. She feels she might have been much better off if she hadn't consulted Bernie at all and had just gone ahead with her instinct and the necessary O.R. processing.

# 19
# Carol

Alison is about to bed down in the closetlike room reserved for residents, but Carol Carse, the black medical student, wants to talk.

Medical students have no reserved room. Sometimes they steal the mattress from a stray stretcher parked in the hall and lie down on the linoleum floor of the second-floor lab. Sometimes they sneak into an unoccupied bed in an empty patients' room.

Alison sits on the low, narrow, foldaway cot in her green scrubs, which she will wear to bed like pajamas. If called urgently out of bed from a dead sleep, she has already circumvented the precious time it would take her to dress and can run like a fireman to wherever the phone summons her.

Following tradition, Carol performs the hospital "scut" work for Alison: changing dressings, inserting nasogastric tubes, starting I.V.'s, and evaluating patients before the resident is called. In return, Alison supervises Carol's work, answers her questions, explains the problems and the course of a patient's treatment, and endeavors to sharpen Carol's overall medical judgment in this first round of a student's clinical training.

Alison is eager to catch a few winks, not knowing what trauma the night will propel into the Emergency Room. But she senses that Carol has a problem on her mind and is unwilling to cut her short.

"Ferguson asked me if he would ever be able to have kids," says Carol thoughtfully. She wears a white jacket—her name tag simply states her name, with no "M.D."—over blue tie-dye slacks, and long, dark hair streams down her back. She is slightly heavy, with a pleasant face which is not traditionally pretty, although there is something attractive about her. Outwardly she seems even-keeled, as if nothing could possibly upset her. "I told him, 'It's possible that you might never be able to have an erection.' "

"Even if the bullet just bounced off the vertebrae, Jake Pell says he's finished," says Alison, flicking her fingers.

"He claims his girlfriend is pregnant and that's why he is so depressed. He won't be able to run and play with his son." Carol shrugs, not quite believing the pregnant-girlfriend story. "Another time he told me his girlfriend couldn't get pregnant and asked me for the name of a good GYN man to see."

With time, Carol intends to specialize in family practice. She leans up against the door of the small, overheated room, seeming to be partly telling Alison her thoughts, partly mulling things over in her own mind. She changes the subject. "I worked with a pediatrician at University Hospital who has a big private practice," she begins. "He told me the kids come in with simple colds and he gives them penicillin. 'If I don't give them penicillin, I know the guy down the street will. You'd be a fool not to do it. You wouldn't last two years that way. You've got to do what your patients want.' "

Alison, sarcastically: "He has a $150,000 house in a swank suburb, nine kids, and a Cadillac."

Carol continues, "If he says, 'Why don't you take some aspirin and drink a lot of juices and your cold will be better,' then they run to the next doctor. It's a virus, they get a shot, and the next day they're better."

"A twenty-four-hour virus." Alison laughs contemptuously. " 'If you leave it alone it will take a week, if treated effectively it will take seven days.' "

Carol's eyes shine with cynicism.

"I don't know," Alison says softly. "This is something for you to decide alone, Carol. If you attack the people on the outside, they're going to be defensive. It will be easier for me if I'm on an academic salary. Then it won't matter how many patients I appease or how many I throw out of the E.R."

Carol is almost talking to herself. "Then there was the orthopedist we were assigned to observe in his private offices. He performed laminectomies for slipped disks on two patients. He knew these particular patients might not get any better, but he had to appease them. The patients might have nothing wrong, but he would give them a shot of steroids in the shoulder, or an Ace bandage, or something.''

''Seven-eighths of all doctors are governed by their patients,'' interrupts Alison, matter-of-factly.

''What should I do?'' Carol is perplexed by the practicalities of her profession. ''And I'm going into family practice.''

She looks out across the room, not at Alison directly. ''This pediatrician said I was crazy not to do it. 'If you don't do it, the pediatrician down the block will do it.' He told me I would change.''

Carol has slowly come to the shadow of a decision. ''I guess I'm going to have to fall into the prescribing bag myself just to please the patients. Give them something benign so they won't go to a doctor who might hurt them. I'll probably develop my own brand of pills—probably a little sugar and aspirin.''

The women say good night, and Alison quickly shuts off the light, pulling the thin blanket snugly over her shoulders.

Carol ambles, unpressed, to the nurses' station with the intention of riffling through her books. The area is darkened, empty, and quiet.

More so than ever, Carol, at twenty-seven, is very much aware of where she has come from and what she will do with her life.

''I'm going to go to a doctor-shortage area,'' she reflects that night. ''Rural Alabama or the North Carolina country. Hopefully I'll have a partner or two because I'll be overwhelmed with work. I've already talked to one guy about it, but his wife doesn't want to move there. Most of my black classmates are in monetary medicine and will practice in middle-class areas. If a fellow is from the ghetto, there is even less reason for him to go back. He is looking for some type of escape. If he goes back, he will depreciate himself vis-à-vis his comrades.

''In southern North Carolina, the need may be so great that it won't matter if I'm a woman. I prefer rural areas because as a woman practicing in the ghetto I have to consider that I might be raped. Or robbed. Drugs are rampant in the ghetto, and people think that a doctor's office is full of drugs.

''Everyone in my practice is going to get checked for everything.

Not long ago I heard of a woman who had been in the hospital for months to find out what was wrong with her. She had a large swelling in the upper arm. A surgeon came up for some reason or another and found a breast mass. By then, it was too late. The cancer was all over the place.'' Carol looks shaken. ''Now I'll do a breast exam on all the women patients who come to see me.

''In working with a patient, I always try to start with a joke. When I had to put a nasogastric tube down Mrs. Parks, I said, 'Now, you've had eleven children. This is going to hurt a lot less than childbirth.'

''The image of the physician is changing. It used to be that physicians were God. Now the patients challenge. Why did the doctor prescribe that drug and what were the indications? Patients *have* to ask questions. They assume too much, but now the younger people aren't going to accept that.

''It's important to educate your patients to take care of themselves. I'm going to have pamphlets in my office with all sorts of information. If patients knew exactly what happened to them when they had a coronary, they would anticipate the consequences and take better care of themselves.

''I decided to become a physician when I saw all the stupid mistakes. A friend of my mother was working in a hospital, and I wanted to see what the life was like so I worked as a hospital volunteer. Five people were on dialysis machines for renal failure. The nurse left for ten minutes and the machine fouled up. All the blood was pouring out and not going back in. Out of those five people, three people died.

''My mother was always interested in nursing and had minimal training. It was enough to get her kids through the childhood illnesses so she didn't have to call the doctor all the time.

''We lived in a low-income housing project and people were always coming over. 'What do you do for this?' 'What do you do for that?' Father John's Medicine was a favorite remedy. I think it's still on the market. She rubbed on Vicks VapoRub, which she mixed with something else. My grandmother was like that, too. Always growing herbs, which she would pull out of the garden.

''When I go home, it's horrible. Someone is always coming in there to talk to me about an ailment. I hate to go there. People call me at 2:00 in the morning. I automatically answer the phone. My family knows not to bother.

"When my father retired, he was earning $6,000 a year. I come from a lower-middle-class family and I went to public schools here in the North. My father's family had been in farming in the South, but there was nothing to do down there so he moved up North in 1932. He got his first job at a school as a cook. He says that a white man gave him his first job. At that time you were a better black, a good person, if your skin was less dark. 'High yellow' they called it. At that time a lot of companies had black supervisors, and they wouldn't hire my father because he was too dark. The only solution was to go to a white person. Later he worked as a stockroom clerk, and he says that some of the advances he got were through the white man.

"There's a lot of religious overlay in the attitudes toward whites in the South. My parents taught me not to be partial to anybody. Treat everyone the same. We are all God's children. In the South, the white man isn't blamed as much as up here. 'Your great-grandfather made my great-grandfather a slave.' In the South, the blacks think that the white man is the same as everybody else. You should love everybody, regardless of what they do to you, and if you believe in God, he will change things. But the younger folk are beginning to reject the religious concept of race relations.

"I do think it's defeatist to bring things up from the past. My parents taught me to think of today or tomorrow.

"As a child in the early sixties, I was bitter because my mother was working in someone else's kitchen. The average black family is maternally oriented. The black woman is out there struggling with two families—the family she is working for and her own. The white woman sits at home reading a book and scheduling luncheons.

"I have a negative image of the women's movement. It's my impression that some movement women are bitter about something in the past. A boyfriend who jilted them. An affair that didn't go well.

"There are roles which are definitely designed for men, like construction work. I don't think that two different sexes would have been made if a woman could do a man's job. F.B.I. work, for instance, is a man's job.

"But this was a bad period in my life when I was reading about slavery. My mother was cooking for that lady and she was running around. My mother explained that she didn't have any education. 'I can't do anything else,' she said. 'Things will get better. They can't get much worse.'

"I have too many demands in my life for most fellows. I'm on every third night and home from the hospital at 8:00. That's a lot for the fellows I have met to put up with. And unless they are a lawyer or something, they feel very uncomfortable. There are many less black men than white men who have professional degrees. The average black fellow doesn't want someone on his level. But if I don't get married sometime soon, I'll adopt some kids."

She thinks for a moment. "If there are any kids left to adopt.

"Some of the worst racism I've ever encountered is in medical school." Her voice sounds tight and choked.

"This was the first medical school which accepted me. Now there are more qualified blacks from Cornell and Harvard. They take the Ivy League blacks first. I'd have much more trouble getting in now.

"The whole idea of letting blacks in was financial gain. We heard they lowered their M.C.A.T. [Medical College Admission Test, a grueling eight-hour test on which medical school admissions are mostly based] guidelines for us. They were forced by the threat of withdrawal of government funding and legal strong-arming to accept people they didn't want to accept. Also the black community was onto them; they saw this bourgeois hospital over there with no blacks on its staff.

"The medical school was getting $2,000 a year from the government for regular students in need and $5,000 a year for minority students, although I'll be $7,000 in debt by the time I graduate. 'Now we're going to open our doors and let some of those dummies in.' Seventeen blacks were admitted. By the end of the freshman year, four were left; by the end of sophomore year, there were three. One of the three licked the dean's tail. He was a dean's spy on the blacks.

"We were all interviewed by psychiatrists, which couldn't be any coincidence. 'How do you feel about your mother?' They practically showed you Rorschach tests. The psychiatrist wanted me to give him an outline of my life and to tell him what I would do if I were an academic failure. Considering my background, could I survive under the most pressure I had ever felt in my life both socially and academically, but especially academically?

"Since I'm a member of two minority groups, black and female, he asked me what did I think about marriage?

"I told him that I had no thought of getting married at the present; that I couldn't say that I would never get married; that women had demonstrated that they could be both a doctor and a spouse. I felt both careers were important, and I wouldn't neglect my patients or give up my practice. If I really studied as I had been accustomed to doing—I was a B-plus student in a public high school in the ghetto and a B student at a white college—I knew I was not at a disadvantage and I felt I would succeed.

"One woman I met who is a black endocrinologist at a veterans' hospital applied to this big white medical school in 1962. During her admissions interview they asked, 'And what do you think of Little Rock, Arkansas?' Now *what* does *that* have to do with being a physician or medical school? They just didn't want to let anybody in there who was going to make waves. She stormed out of there in a steam and applied to Howard University's medical school. She claims that people see your color first, then your sex.

"The expectation was that we wouldn't do well, and when we did, they were amazed.

"Many of us ended up below the curve, with below-average grades, not knowing where the cutoff point was.

"They told us to sit in the front of the class and be more attentive and take better notes. We wouldn't be distracted and talk to each other.

"They ask us why we always sit together in the cafeteria."

Her voice is choked. "The first two years I always expected to be called first in class even though it is supposed to be alphabetical.

"One fellow had an advanced science degree and he failed freshman biochemistry. It hit him very badly. He went out of his head and dropped out.

"Every time we took an exam, the proctors would come over and stand next to us to make sure we weren't cheating. Now the medical school has set up a special tutoring system to help blacks.

"The residents may distribute xeroxes of articles from medical journals to the medical students to help them with their patients. Then I ask for one. 'I don't have any. You should to go the library.'

"Some of the residents give me patients with no pathology, a patient recuperating from a heart attack, for instance. You're just supposed to ask how they feel. It wouldn't do any good if I complained. They would say something like, 'We're just giving you patients as they come up.'

"Sometimes a resident won't answer my question. I was asking one resident about a boy who had a rash from ampicillin. Was it an allergic reaction to the antibiotics or the manifestation of an infection due to the disease? 'We can talk about it later. We're on rounds now, so let's hurry up.'

"The attending surgeons may pick on you or try to embarrass you in front of everyone or ignore you completely and assume you don't know it anyway. So why bother to talk to you.

"During a medical conference, the teacher had eye contact with everyone but me. I think you can tell a lot from eye contact. In front of the patients, one attending even went to the point of calling me *Miss* Carse.'' Carol laughs softly. ''What can you do? After all, you're only a medical student.

"On a lot of occasions when I presented a case on rounds and a question was put to me about it, another medical student or a resident would shout the answer before I'd get a chance to answer myself.

"Later, the comments on my student evaluation ran, 'Fund of knowledge is barely acceptable.'

"At first I thought I had to work harder, but then I saw that it didn't make any difference.

"On occasion a patient will say, 'Who are you?' or 'My doctor didn't tell me about you.' One woman who was dying of cancer said, ' *You're* not going to start that I.V., are you?' I told her, 'If that's the way you feel, I won't do it. I'll walk out.'

"Sometimes I can feel some reverse prejudice, I suppose by the discomfort of the patients when I go in their rooms. I can see they are afraid. 'Here comes another one who probably hates whites. What is she going to do to me?' They are afraid I am going to hurt them when I give them medical treatment.

"That first year of medical school, all the black students were steadily going downhill. The ass-kisser told the dean we were going to a newspaper. One day they called our names: 'Will the following people please stay after the lecture?' And of course it was all of us.

" 'What's all this disaffection among you I'm hearing about? If you go to a newspaper, you're putting your career on the line. We can let you out. There are plenty of people who want to come in.' They could blackball you so you couldn't get an internship.

"There is one woman professor who couldn't understand why we were having so much trouble. She feels that if we flunk a test twice we should be kicked out. If we don't have the background, we shouldn't be in there. I hate that woman. I once asked her about summer jobs. She has connections coming out of her ears. I wanted to be a lab technician for that summer. 'Oh, I just don't know anybody. Times are really hard.' Another girl went in and she gave her a list of summer jobs. I ended up working that summer as a salesgirl in the candy store at Sears.

''I haven't liked some of the remarks I've heard about women, but I don't comment about it anymore. I learned to live with words after my brother was a member of the first integrated class in his school and he got into a couple of fights.

''Sometimes you hear comments like, 'What is this? There are so many women around here we're beginning to look like Russia.'

''I remember one resident who headed the women's medicine ward at an army hospital. He hated women. Any complaint was psychosomatic. Any woman between the ages of twenty-five and forty who had chest pains, it was probably anxiety. They were all women and they were always complaining. This lady had lost a whale of a lot of weight and all the tests were negative. Give her Valium. Give them 10 mg. of Valium and make them shut up.

''I didn't like my OB-GYN rotation very much. I went to tell the resident that I thought one woman was about to have her baby. It wasn't her first one, so she could tell. The nurse thought so, too. He said, 'Oh, let her suffer a little more. She isn't ready.' He left to make a phone call and the baby was there. Let them suffer. If you're going to do that, have natural childbirth, then what's the point of coming to a hospital? Let them suffer.

''Gynecologists talk a lot about women. 'She had such big boobs. You could put your fist in her vagina, she had screwed so many times.' If there were tears along the cervical and vaginal areas—a lot of people insert things in there—they would make jokes about that.

''The attitude of some of the doctors toward older people isn't the best either. There's a lot of experimenting with older people just for the experience, regardless of the consequences. Sometimes I've seen them order tests without any regard to the cost for the patient. A doctor came in who specializes only in the digestive tract. He asked for work-ups which cost $1,000 and never came up with a diagnosis —that's how a few doctors make money, by ordering any type of test they want whether it's pertinent or not.

''I'll keep my patients away from specialists. When you're in family practice, you have to worry about the cost to the patient.

"I think one thing that will be with us for a long time is the attitude toward poor black women. Any black girl in the clinic, if she has abdominal pain, it is *assumed* that she has P.I.D. [pelvic inflammatory disease, usually associated with gonorrhea]. She's asked if she has been playing around. That'll be with us for a long time.

"As the only black girl in my class, I missed not having another black woman to talk to. There are some things that are easier to talk about to a girl than a fellow. A lot of the other girls were close—they roomed together—but I always felt uncomfortable at their social affairs, which I usually avoided. Everybody would sit around and talk about their travels to Europe or elsewhere, and I've never traveled.

"There was one black girl the first year who later dropped out when she became pregnant. She wouldn't give me the time of day. She drove a Cadillac to school. I drove a crummy car and lived in a crummy house.

"My mother is older and I couldn't talk to her, and my father wouldn't understand. My sister is a school-bus driver and my brother is a plumber, and I couldn't talk to them either.

"If I have any advice for a black girl coming into medicine, it would be that she can't be too emotional or she won't survive. I would tell her to ignore a lot of comments. Hold your head up high. Study first. Try to get above-average grades on exams. Put studying the first year above all else. Sit in the front row because you're automatically going to be called first, so you might as well sit there so you don't have to come to the front—or else you might be totally ignored. Be very careful what you say, because it might get to the wrong ears and be held against you."

A nurse interrupts and asks Carol to insert an I.V. into an aged man who, even though his arms are tied, is systematically managing to pull out his I.V.'s.

The gaunt, hollow-cheeked man sitting up in bed has prostatic cancer, which has invaded his bone marrow.

White cloth straps are tied loosely around his wrists. Some red, infected bedsores are visible under the white hospital gown.

"I'm going to tell your daughter on you," scolds Carol affectionately, "and she might give you a whipping."

The toothless mouth, which forms a wrinkled, concave hole, voices no answer.

Carol is shouting her questions. "How old are you, Pops?"

The age-freckled face framed with snow-white hair lights up for the first time. His translucent eyes seem to sparkle.

"Ninety-nine years old," he replies without pressing his lips together or seeming to use his tongue.

As Carol struggles with the I.V., groans of pain seem to rise from the man's gut.

While a nurse watches, ready to help, Carol is successful in putting the I.V. into the old man's flesh, transparent and thin like tissue paper. "You're a good boy!

"What are your daughters' names, Pops?"

The old man's clear blue eyes sparkle with mischief. "We don't call them by names—by numbers." The words are not fully articulated and he communicates with a moaning sound.

The taut, wrinkled skin around his mouth stretches almost imperceptibly into the suggestion of a smile.

His eyes focus on Carol Carse and follow her out the door.

# 20
# Nights

It is 8:30 P.M. in the patients' waiting area of the Emergency Room. An elderly man has thoughtfully brought his supper in a brown paper bag. He must have been waiting a long, long time, for the bag looks as rumpled as he does. A scattering of people wait patiently and acceptingly, staring silently at the empty space in front of them. Occasionally a loud voice calls out a name. It booms from behind a cinder-block wall which separates the waiting room from the stretcher area. A man with a single crutch hobbles over to the glass-enclosed desk at one end of the E.R. to spark the tedious admissions paperwork; the admitting clerk is interviewing a woman who seems to be sunken into her chair. Another man holds a thick wad of tissues to his eye. He sits uncomplainingly, while a woman attempts to comfort two tearful, impatient children. Pay phones line one side of the drab beige walls and cigarette butts carpet the floors.

The damaged condition in which some of the area's people stumble into the E.R. never ceases to amaze Alison. How can they let their condition deteriorate so desperately before coming to seek help? One woman arrives complaining moderately of stomach pain. At the time, the residents think her problem might be ulcers. What she has is a galloping advanced cancer. They can't even find the primary cause, and she dies within five weeks of admission.

Examining another woman, who complains of rectal bleeding, Alison finds an enormous fungating carcinoma which is well within the range of a rectal exam. Alison is disgusted the tumor was initially missed. It wasn't even a hard diagnosis. People who have advanced cancer *look* as though they have cancer. She looks cachectic, pathetically wasted, washed-out.

One emaciated man wants to know why his teeth are falling out. He has advanced carcinoma of the upper palate, a big white growth which fills the back of his jaw and grotesquely swells his cheeks.

"It's incredible," Alison says. "The cancer is inoperable now. When radiation has shrunk the mass a bit, a surgical team can remove his mandible, tongue, and larynx. The question is, does anyone want such a radical operation?"

At City Hospital Alison is handling pathology that doctors don't normally see in the outside world. People don't let their health slip so far except in poverty areas. Here the patients happen through the hospital's double glass doors only with insistent or excruciating pain. One has to be in pain to sit there in the emergency room waiting for so many hours to be heard.

Mrs. Hall, the fifty-two-year-old mother of eight children, is such a person. She has arrived on the second surgical floor with a raging peritonitis, which has spread to the entire abdominal cavity. The abdominal wall is so soft and relaxed that her bladder has dropped and ballooned out of her vagina. The E.R. residents initially took one look at *that* and thought she was a gynecological case; for several days she was essentially misclassified on the gynecological service.

"The bladder," Alison reports to Dave, "actually looks like a scrotum."

Carol, too, is taken aback. "Why," she asks an older teen-age son, "did you let her go so long before coming in?"

"She was afraid of doctors and what they would do to her," the young man tells her.

Going under anesthesia for emergency surgery, Mrs. Hall has vomited and aspirated her own vomit into her lungs, the acid biting and damaging the mucosal lining of her bronchial tubes and lungs, causing a condition officially described as bilateral aspiration pneumonia. Involving both lungs, the chemical irritation is resistant to most treatments and impossible to flush out. This accidental setback has markedly dimmed Mrs. Hall's chances of survival.

"A patient vomiting and aspirating the vomit on the O.R. table while going under anesthesia is a big no-no," says Alison, who has assisted in the O.R. at 2:00 A.M. She wonders if the anesthesiologist has injected Mrs. Hall with sodium pentothol, relaxing the abdominal muscles so the stomach's contents could wash back past the sphincters into the throat, without previously connecting the suction apparatus that would draw the gastric contents out of her mouth in case of such an accident. Mrs. Hall inhaled some of her own vomit during the time the suction was being connected.

Alison and Dave decide to continue with the surgery. Mrs. Hall has come into their care rigid with pain. It turns out that an unnatural perforation in her large bowel has contaminated her entire peritoneal cavity. Alison and Dave are anxious to open their patient, close the perforation, drain the peritoneal cavity of pus and abscesses, diagnose her problem, and hopefully plan a course of treatment. But the problem they now discover is a perforated rectal cancer, and the cancer is rampant.

Afterward the young residents discover that she was previously another university's patient in the same hospital. Following the usual admissions procedure, she should be in a different surgical wing. Alison and Dave decide to keep Mrs. Hall. They can't bring themselves to call up and say, "We just operated on your patient and she is about to die."

All of Mrs. Hall's eight children are here, ranging in age from ten to twenty-six years. The older children take turns rushing excitedly back and forth from the waiting room outside the unit into the I.C.U., not comprehending what is happening to their mother. The nurses seem annoyed over the confusion and noise. There is no husband that Alison can see, and a daughter, somewhere in her mid-twenties, seems to be in charge. Alison draws the daughter away into a corner.

"I told the family that their mother was a very, very sick woman and that they would not see all those doctors rushing in for a resuscitation." Alison explains later, rubbing her eyes. "Is it worth it to revive her only to have her die of cancer? Cancer is not a very pleasant thing." Alison frankly wishes a speedy death for her patient. "You can't actually write 'Don't code' on the sheet, but there is no way I am going to call in a resuscitation team.

"In treating the family of a terminal patient, you tell them in veiled fashion that you will not go to heroic efforts to revive their relative and they get the idea. Then it's not their fault, it's your fault. Families don't want that on their conscience. If someone is dying of cancer—and it's an ugly death—and he has heart failure, I'm not doing him a favor by resuscitating him. You might admit someone just to die, since it's very hard on the family. Some patients basically just need a place to die.'' The decision not to have Mrs. Hall resuscitated is made jointly by the senior and first-year resident who form City Hospital's nighttime team on the surgical floor.

Trying to snatch some sleep, Alison has just eased herself into a comfortable position when the I.C.U. calls, the ring of the phone blasting in her ears. Mrs. Hall's pulse rate has slowed dramatically, her blood pressure has dropped ominously, and her breathing is labored. Alison says the I.C.U. nurses are telling her that Mrs. Hall is just about dead.

Rushing to the I.C.U., Alison and Dave are both horrified to discover that Mrs. Hall's family has decamped for the night; Mrs. Hall's thread of a life will never last until morning. The nurses, irritated by the excitable family disrupting their clockwork routine, asked Carol Carse to get rid of them. Alison suspects that the nurses probably did not realize that Carol, who wears a short white jacket like the residents, was a medical student. So Carol dutifully told the offspring that they could no longer stay, and why not come back in the morning?

Alison chides Carol. ''You should call us about something like that. Under the circumstances, the family should be able to go into the I.C.U. whenever they want to.'' Carol, for whom personal rapport with the patients means so much, is shattered.

Dave and Alison step outside the I.C.U. and put their heads together. Should they keep Mrs. Hall alive so that her family can say good-bye?

''If you chronically don't get any sleep as a resident,'' says Alison, ''you're hurting for sleep. So the question is, Should I keep her alive for another seven hours? Or how can I arrange to get some sleep? It's not a very fine thing to admit to. But you have to think very realistically what your position is so you can rest.''

Dave, who tries to arrange one entire free weekend a month with his family, doubles up his on-call hours. At City Hospital, senior residents are normally ''on'' every other night, so that now he has worked here for sixty unbroken hours: all day and night Friday, all day and night Saturday, and today is Sunday.

Basically Alison is in favor of pushing the chemical stimulants so that Mrs. Hall's family can get there before the final breath. Some people have a desperate need to see their relative before the end, even though there is nothing they can do. Among her directives to the nurses, Alison leaves orders for dopamine to be administered to revive blood pressure, atropine to stimulate the heartbeat. They are keeping Mrs. Hall technically alive.

When the eldest daughter sees her mother in a comatose state, she breaks down into crying hysterics. Her siblings become hysterical, too.

Keeping a professional front, Alison feels very inadequate. She can't bring herself to say "Don't worry, everything will be fine," because she knows it won't be. She can't say "I know how you feel" either, because she *doesn't* really know how they feel.

At 10:00 A.M. Mrs. Hall dies, and one of the I.C.U. nurses draws the curtain around the bed. Mrs. Hall's family had been allowed into the bustle of the I.C.U. five minutes out of every half hour, and she died while they were waiting for their next turn inside. In a few hours the bed will be ready for the following patient and the new morning's admission.

Before Mrs. Hall was operated on, Dave took a picture of her physical condition—the prolapsed bladder which looked like a scrotum. He had never seen anything like it, and the picture would make a useful teaching aid.

Alison literally rolls out of bed at the ring of the phone. 5:45 A.M. Adam Wilkens, an eighteen-year-old black male, has been shot in the calf and is now admitted to the surgical floor from the Emergency Room. Alison must elicit the preliminary history and physical which is routine upon admission. She must decipher what might be wrong with the patient's overall system—he may have a seizure disorder, for instance—in case his condition deteriorates over the next few hours.

In the all-male ward, dim-lit and hushed, Adam Wilkens is stretched out in a new hospital gown and nearly asleep under a clean white sheet. Young and muscular, resting his head on his arm, he glances up indifferently at Alison, who neglects to introduce herself. For all he knows she could be another one of the nurses, and he has already been interviewed downstairs in the Emergency Room.

"Mr. Wilkens, I want to know about your leg." Alison stares at blank lined paper, ready to write down his medical story, which is not forthcoming.

"What can you tell me about your leg?"

"Nothing." He wants to be left alone.

"That's a big help. What kind of angle were they shooting at you from? Up or down?"

Silence from Mr. Wilkens, who lies on the bed with his eyes closed.

"Mr. Wilkens, you were shot last night. Did they fire just one shot?"

"The bullet came in and the bullet came out."

"They found the bullet?"

"Uh, huh."

"Why were you here before?" His patient number indicates a previous admission at the same hospital.

"I don't know."

"When were you here?"

"When I was young."

"Did your family tell you why you were here?"

"Because I was shot." His answers are short and groggy with sleep.

"Were you old enough to remember the other time?"

"I was old enough to remember, but I don't know."

Alison decides to pursue another line of questioning. "Do you have trouble with headaches? Difficulty in your ears? Difficulty hearing? Do you take any medications? Do you have any medical problems?"

No answer.

"Do you get frequent sore throats?"

"Uh, huh."

"Any hoarseness?"

"Huh? Uh, huh." Wilkens intermittently opens, rolls, and closes his eyes. He exudes nonchalance and boredom.

"How far can you walk? Can you run up the stairs?"

"I think so. I'm not sure about it." He opens and closes his eyes and manifests an erection.

Alison doesn't seem to notice, and he shows no change of facial expression.

"Any difficulty with broken bones?"

"I ain't had no broken bones. I'm hungry."

"Were you in any other hospital?"

"I was in. . . ." His sentence trails off into a low mutter.

"Where?"

"Here."

"Are you allergic to any medicines, particularly penicillin?"

No answer.

"Do you smoke?"

"Uh, huh."

"How much?"

"A little."

"A pack a day?"

No answer.

"Are your mother and father still alive?"

The heavy-lidded, expressionless young man seems to fall groggily to sleep.

"Are you in good health?" Alison pokes Adam Wilkens in the ribs with her ballpoint pen.

"Mr. Wilkens, Mr. Wilkens. Do you have any brothers and sisters?"

"Seven brothers and sisters. . . . Shi-i-it."

"How far did you get in school?"

"Ninth grade."

"Are you unemployed?"

"Yes."

"Are you married?"

"Whaaa?"

"Are you married?"

"No."

"Does your leg hurt a lot or are you just scared?"

"I'm tired. Where's my mother?"

"Where did you leave her last? Did you call her?"

"No. Ummmmm."

Alison peels back the sheet and begins the physical examination, feeling his abdomen, the femoral pulse in his groin, checking to see if the femoral pulse is present and equal in both legs. Again he has an erection. Again they both seem equally indifferent. In turn she feels the pulse in his foot and behind the knees, checking the circulation in his legs, and listens to his heart and lungs. Nothing abnormal.

With one quick movement, she rips off the bandage taped to his calf. There are two small, angry red marks about four inches apart, the entry and exit points of the bullet's trajectory.

"They were shooting down like this?" Alison gestures to the ground, holding and pointing her hand as if it were a gun. The E.R. report states there is no apparent motor damage to Wilkens' leg.

She proceeds with the routine genital and rectal exam. He has another erection.

"I didn't say anything and he didn't say anything," Alison reports later as she slips back into her cot for a few more moments of soothing sleep before early-morning rounds. "It's more frequent in young kids."

When asked why she is going to nap rather than complete the questionnaire and fill in the gaps, she shoots back quickly, shaking her head in disgust, "If he were old and had heart disease—then I would do a history because he wouldn't last the night."

Adam Wilkens and Alison Merrill have something in common— they both want to sleep.

Alison has learned to conserve sapped energy and ease chronic lack of sleep when necessary. Only a half hour of rest before the next hospital day begins.

# 21
# The End of Mr. Lincoln

It is a pitiful semblance of life. At eighty-eight, Edwin Lincoln is speechless from several strokes, rigid with age and disease, and curled up like a pretzel on his stretcher. He has traveled a long road into senility and his family has abandoned him in the Emergency Room.

City Hospital is the poor and aged's sometime warehouse, and the Emergency Room their dumping ground. Waiting lists for the city's nursing homes are endless; the acute medical problems of the area's senior citizens frequently overpower their families. City Hospital's dreary, overloaded Emergency Room is the end of the road. Although it was not yet apparent on admission, Mr. Lincoln has been sent away to die.

During the first round, Mr. Lincoln is admitted without any questions. Since he is a Home Care patient, he can be admitted directly to the hospital on the recommendation of his Home Care physician. Large, gaping ulcers surround his pelvis, flesh eroding from bone, the result of long, unchanging confinement in bed, the pressure of his body rubbing continually against the bedsheets. The open sores are red and infected.

The admitting doctor examines Mr. Lincoln and scratches the salient facts on an E.R. sheet: "Home Care victim with multiple infected decubiti; residual paralysis of (L) arm and leg. Rheumatoid arthritis. Lesions are infected. Left heel revealed a massive excavation of the flesh."

A victim of circumstance, of disease, Mr. Lincoln is sent to the surgical floor, where the treatment of decubiti, or bedsores, is reluctantly relegated. The surgical residents are not normally overjoyed with the duty of treating bedsores, because there is very little they feel they can do. In the bedridden patient, any skin grafts will eventually erode. "No service likes this kind of problem," says Alison, "because it's very un-ego-gratifying, and there's a lot of ego gratification in medicine." Mr. Lincoln himself is unable to make any pronouncements about his cursory shuttling to the second floor. After his several strokes, his brain no longer connects with his mouth.

The nurses and an orderly lift him onto his waiting bed near a window. Mr. Lincoln has come to roost in the far right corner of the long male ward. He will be fed and bathed. His bedsores will be duly treated with Elase solution to soften and clean out the dead tissue in order to begin eradicating the painful infection.

A week later, Alison Merrill is on the phone with the hospital social worker at the central nurses' station, coping with a special emergency, someone whose medical care can no longer be handled at home. She swings around in her chair to face Dave and outline the problem. "The man has had thoracic surgery for cancer. The cancer has probably metastasized to the brain. He's incontinent, and his wife has had several strokes. As debilitated as she is, the social worker doesn't think she's capable of taking care of him. If we admit him just to take a look, we can't have an ambulance take him back." Although an ambulance trip from the home to the hospital is considered an emergency, rating medical coverage, there are no funds to cover the cost of the homebound trip. Obviously this man cannot be simply sent back home in a cab because his wife would be unable to help him up the stairs to their apartment.

Alison sighs, holding the receiver to one side. "I hate to admit him as a social emergency because that means he's with us for an eternity."

It sounds cruel, but Alison worries that the much-needed bed on a full floor will be occupied by someone who is essentially misclassified for the surgical service, taking up the space for another patient who needs surgery. There is always a shortage of beds on the surgical floor. In fact, several of the university's surgical beds on this floor are filled with patients from another university service which, in turn, did not have any open beds on its floor. Fayard thinks for a minute. "I think from what we saw of him at clinic, we can admit him. Go ahead."

"Medicine isn't always the way you see it on TV," says Alison resignedly. "I used to see Marcus Welby fetching his patients in their rooms, pushing their wheelchairs, then waving good-bye at the door. If patients didn't show up at the hospital when they were due, Marcus Welby arrived at their homes to see why. Who the hell has time to do that in the real world? A nurses' aide or even a volunteer is the one to push a wheelchair." Seeing a doctor push a wheelchair is a little like seeing a corporation president type his own correspondence.

For the next hour, Alison looks for a vial of operating room cultures which was lost between the O.R. and Bacteriology, or BAC T, as the residents refer to that lab. The cultures were removed in the O.R. from the chest of a fifteen-year-old girl repeatedly stabbed with a five-inch serrated steak knife by a school mate during a heated argument over a boyfriend. The O.R. nurses promised they would reach BAC-T that day; the older the cultures, the less accurate the laboratory results.

Headed for the BAC-T lab, Alison runs down the stairs, hurries down the oppressive basement corridor where the floor seems to undulate in waves, sinking deeper and deeper into the ground. A white-coated technician is sorry, but BAC-T has not yet received the cultures. "It's really bad if the cultures get so old you can't use them." Pressed, she goes to check whether they might have been left in the pathology lab by mistake. Less time to check on patients, less time to write up charts. A check with both BAC-T and Pathology does not turn up the operating room specimens, and Alison feels discouraged.

In the basement, she decides to wander by Radiology and finds Sam Ferguson waiting his turn on a long line of stretchers outside the door to X-ray. Alison is worried that Ferguson has something alarming going on in his abdomen. The question is what. Infection? Adhesions? An ileus, or blockage of the intestinal tract? Having ordered an upright X-ray so she can differentiate the abdomen's air and fluid levels, she wants to make sure the X-ray table is properly raised, with Ferguson correctly strapped, for a vertically positioned picture. He can't stand up by himself, of course, and the X-ray technician will have to go to extra trouble just to fix Ferguson to the table. It will be easier for the overworked X-ray technician not to do it. In fact, Alison pretty well knows when she orders an upright X-ray that the technician probably won't do it. A good amount of her day is spent walking from place to place to make sure the lab work she ordered will be carried through. She is determined to see her patient's upright body on that table.

Ferguson looks considerably more tired, thinner, than he did immediately after he was shot. His flesh seems more flaccid, his face appears to sag. Perhaps it is simply the loss of hope. Dejected, Ferguson spends a great deal of time staring silently from his bed.

At his request, Alison draws a picture of the area the X-ray technician will photograph.

"I have to face reality," Ferguson says softly.

"That's right," she answers quickly. She gives Ferguson her drawing. "O.K. Looks good. See you a little later."

She sighs, leaving his side. "What can I do? You can't misrepresent. That's what you have to do."

Ferguson is fifth on a line which stretches down the hallway outside X-ray. There is no formal waiting room, just the narrow corridor with the stretchers parked one behind the other against the long far wall.

Alison's time is too precious to waste standing idle. She decides to check further with the operating room nurses to see if she can discover those cultures. Upstairs on the second floor the nurses assure her the cultures were picked up by a messenger.

As she walks up to the second-floor nurses' station, she sees Don Wilder, with Schmidt and Armstrong by his side, staring across the counter at head nurse Val Sanders.

"Can you put Edwin Lincoln on a stretcher?" he asks.

Usually even-tempered, Val Sanders glares at the floor. A nurse refusing so defiantly to carry out a doctor's orders is a strange thing indeed.

Medical student Kirstin Fernie, chewing gum, stops to watch.

"We're refusing to do it," Val Sanders states. Her voice is steel although she has not actually raised her tone. "Point-blank. No." She crosses her arms, Mr. Lincoln's folder cradled protectively against her chest. Leaning her back against one of the pillars, she seems inflexible, her spine stiff with indignation. Ordinarily she is more like an automaton, effecting doctors' orders without flagrant challenge. There is very little social interchange between the young rotating residents and the permanent, full-time nursing staff, between doctor and nurse, between white and black.

"I need an extra bed," snorts Val Sanders, not lifting her eyes from the floor, refusing eye contact with the residents, offering her solution to the bed shortage with a request to increase the total number. But Schmidt, Armstrong, and Wilder manage to find a stretcher and to heave Mr. Lincoln onto it. Schmidt, always impeccably dressed—today he wears a wide green bow tie, a matching green vest, a yellow shirt, and a green wool tweed sports coat—seems outwardly unflappable.

With his knees flexed to his chest, his head halfcocked, Edwin Lincoln is pushed to the nurses' station on a stretcher. He is half sitting, with his weight on his elbows. His mouth, as always, is open, perhaps in wonderment, perhaps in pain, perhaps because he wants to say something and can't.

Dave Fayard walks up, surprised to see Mr. Lincoln being disposed of in such a fashion.

"What happened?" asks Fayard, curious.

"We're discharging Mr. Lincoln, dropping him off where he came in," says Wilder, studying Dave's face.

Fayard's expression is something between a smile and a grimace.

Wilder laughs. "You had the same look when I was pounding a patient's chest in the E.R. and you asked what happened. You can help with the stretcher, too."

Craig Armstrong, waiting beside Mr. Lincoln's stretcher to push him on, stares at the ceiling in exasperation and sighs deeply.

Alison looks up from making an entry on a patient's chart. "There's a long history to this."

Now Schmidt, the chief resident, addresses Val Sanders himself. "Put Mr. Bowman"—a new patient—"in his bed."

No answer. Val Sanders doesn't move. The two or three other nurses at the nurses' station are seemingly busy, preoccupied with other matters. But there is a curious, sodden silence from all the nursing staff.

With a sudden movement, Val Sanders throws Mr. Lincoln's metal folder, which she has been gripping so tightly, hurling it across the nurses' station where it slams against a wall and clatters noisily to the floor. The noise is all the more jarring in the momentary quiet.

Mr. Lincoln, his mouth still agape, is rolled down the hall toward the elevators.

Having observed the scene silently, Kirstin asks Alison for details.

Alison speaks sharply. Mr. Lincoln was not admitted as a social emergency but as a Home Care patient, and he should never have been admitted in the first place.

His daughter, knowing something about Home Care procedure, had called the hospital and dropped the names of a few Home Care physicians, falsely stating that her father's admission had been ordered by one of them. Under Home Care provisions, the hospital was obligated to admit him. City Hospital sent an ambulance to pick him up and afterward called Home Care to find out about his case; they found out that his admission had been completely manipulated. But the surgical floor kept him long enough to treat his bedsores and to give the daughter a rest.

Mr. Lincoln's bedsores improved to the point where there was no longer the shadow of a reason for him to stay at the hospital. Although the bedsores would never heal shut, the infection in those areas was gone. Now Surgery needed the bed for someone else. Upon calling his daughter, who is his guardian, the hospital discovered that the family, fed up with the burdens of care for the terminally ill, unequivocally refused to take the father back. Although it was an accepted procedure in the old days for families to nurse their dying relatives until the end, there is nothing more frightening to many people now than to have someone die at home. It may take days, weeks, months—and it is a tremendous strain on the family. And for the surgical residents, there is very little more they can do to improve Mr. Lincoln's permanently impaired medical lot.

Theoretically, Mr. Lincoln should not be a patient at City Hospital anymore. But the family will neither take him back nor approve nursing-home papers because they don't want to get stuck with any of the costs. "You've got to feel sorry for Mr. Lincoln," says Alison, "but all he requires is custodial care. You sympathize with the family and at the same time you're furious with them because they won't take him back."

Under such circumstances, the hospital is entitled to send the patient back to his home. But strictly speaking, the daughter's home is not the father's.

Wilder and the others are forcibly transporting Mr. Lincoln to the Emergency Room, where he will be reregistered. The E.R. will consult the surgical service and they will refuse him for lack of beds. Edwin Lincoln will become another service's patient and problem until a city nursing home is found in a couple of months. He will have to wait his turn until a nursing-home patient either improves or expires.

·   "It's really not fair to us," says Alison. "But the nurses feel that it's a rotten thing to do to someone who has had a stroke, is aphasiac, can't talk, and is all curled up in bed. Basically, they think we're throwing him in the gutter."

An hour later, before the chief resident's rounds, Schmidt sits at the desk in the Surgical Office while the residents and medical students begin to gather around him. His long legs are stretched out comfortably, his feet resting on a wastebasket, waiting for the last stragglers to collect in the room. Craig Armstrong strides in. "Guess who's back?" he asks Schmidt innocently.

Mr. Lincoln is back. He sits in crooked angles on his stretcher, parked carefully to one side of the nurses' station. He moves his head and moans. Is he straining to communicate?

As Armstrong tells Schmidt what has happened, Schmidt becomes quite agitated, pounding his fist on the desk once or twice. The nursing service has taken the responsibility of retrieving Mr. Lincoln's stretcher from the Emergency Room. Mrs. Porter, the surgical nursing supervisor, has even attempted to contact Dr. Hartwick Abney, the university's surgical department head at City Hospital, who spends most of the week in another part of town at University Hospital. Dr. Abney's day-to-day presence is represented by Kate Marra, his efficient, intelligent, understanding secretary, who carefully keeps her eye on the resident brood. The administrative details of many training programs are actually run by the secretaries while the doctors are busy with patient care. Kate is a shining example.

Schmidt is more and more infuriated. It is hard to tell whether he is angry because the nurses overrode his orders or because the whole episode may cost him points with Dr. Abney.

"That pisses me off," he seethes.

He grabs the phone on the desk and calls Kate.

"Hey, Kate, what is this crap? To our surprise, Mr. Lincoln is back on our floor," Schmidt complains into the phone. "Do you know who sent him back?" He pauses and listens. "Well, I'm going to call Mrs. Porter and tell her it was none of her goddamn business. Who is Mrs. Porter, anyway? This was straightened out doctor to doctor. That's not her role to run to Dr. Abney."

"Mrs. Porter didn't call Abney," Armstrong whispers. "Kate did."

"This is a doctor-to-doctor problem," Schmidt continues raging. "The patient has been disposed of. As you know, we have four or five boarders and we're trying to get back their beds."

Schmidt eventually hangs up, disgusted, then tries unsuccessfully to reach Dr. Abney himself. "That really pisses me off," he repeats.

Armstrong shakes his head slowly, looking at the floor, his shoulders bent over in his chair. "I tell you, Bernie, this system makes a nice guy turn bad. You can just get beaten over the head so many times."

Wilder always has room for a joke. He crouches, hiding, behind Schmidt's taller frame. "I want you to know," he says with mock seriousness, "that when you talk to Abney, we'll be right behind you."

"Listen, I'll be with you," Hank Sanchez stresses. "Rebecca Hanley was dumped on us and that was no goddamn learning experience."

"Now you know why I never wear a name tag," cracks Wilder.

Red-haired Kate peers inside the door, then bustles into the group of residents as she is apt to do to gauge their mood at the end of the day.

"Hey, Kate," Wilder calls to her. "We discharged a patient and that goddamn Mrs. Porter brought him back. Now what gave her that authority when we weren't even consulted?"

"The patient you discharged today?"

"Yes."

"Didn't you hear he had no place to go?"

Wilder now stands on top of one of the chairs. He grins. "We heard rumors to that effect."

Several of the residents titter.

"Hey, Kate," Wilder volunteers. "Your hair looks a different color from up here."

Julie objects. "Boy, you're really nice," she says.

Kate leaves without feeling the need to answer.

Outside in the hall after rounds, Schmidt meets Mrs. Porter for the first time. Mrs. Porter is a smiling older woman of matronly contours who exudes cheerful competence.

"Did you bring Mr. Lincoln back to the floor?" Schmidt asks evenly.

"Yes, I did."

"You should have checked with me first," he chides.

"I approve of what you do, not always how you do things," she says quickly, not one to be easily intimidated. Her response sounds like a line she has prepared in advance.

"It was all being taken care of," Schmidt says calmly.

"Not as far as who was going to take care of the patient."

Schmidt has no answer.

Mrs. Porter walks off, her better judgment impelling her to cut the conversation short.

Hank Sanchez helps the nurses hoist Mr. Lincoln from the stretcher back onto his bed. A sudden, full-throated moan gushes from his mouth and twisted body. Pain is one of the few emotions Lincoln can express.

Mission accomplished, Sanchez flexes his arms for the sake of the watching residents, like a muscleman Tarzan lifting weights.

Alison learns that the cultures she was searching for earlier were mislaid, so to speak, in the hematology lab. Since the bacteriology lab is in the furthest subterranean corner of the building, the messenger dropped off the cultures at the nearer hematology office to save himself some time. Alison has learned her lesson there. The next time she will take the cultures down herself.

On another side of the male ward, she sees Sam Ferguson's girlfriend silently, methodically brushing his hair with a pink, plastic hairbrush.

Rounds and Mr. Lincoln's turmoil have taken time away from maneuvering Sam Ferguson through X-ray. Now Alison discovers that he was never properly placed on the X-ray table.

Ignored for the time being, Mr. Lincoln has become a social disposition on the surgical floor; his crippled life is a social burden and his body is awaiting disposition into one of the area's publicly funded nursing homes. Lincoln's eyes are glazed and faded and filmy. A pathetic little pretzel on the city's hospital records.

# 22
# Good-bye at Rounds

Calling often but visiting rarely, Mike almost never sees his surgeon-wife in her hospital setting. Mike doesn't like coming to the hospital and feels out of place. But New Year's Eve is an exception. As luck would have it, Alison is on call that night, and they want to spend their first New Year's Eve as a married couple together.

Checking by phone in advance to make sure she is not inaccessibly sequestered in the operating room, Mike arrives with a $2 bottle of sparkling Burgundy. In the senior resident's private on-call room with its rudimentary bed, desk, and phone, the residents are a little past feeling good on a choice of bourbon and vodka in paper cups. Along with the corn chips, liquid refreshments were collected at the last minute at a neighborhood liquor store. A TV blares loudly. The residents are just as noisy. The atmosphere isn't much to speak of, but when you're tired, a little alcohol goes a long way. No other spouses have come.

Near midnight, a resident is talking to his wife on the phone and the television predictably flashes a picture of New York's Times Square merrymaking. Mike and Alison hug close and smooch, hard, on the mouth.

A faint bleeper goes off, chiming indistinctly. One of the residents lifts the sports jacket he has thrown casually on the bed. BLEEP. BLEEP. BLEEP. Wilson Lane, the paged resident, is called urgently to the Emergency Room. A young girl is waiting, with abdominal injuries which include—as the resident will discover once he opens her up to stop the bleeding—a spleen ruptured in an automobile crash. Slightly tipsy, Wilson Lane will have to perform a splenectomy, the surgical excision of the spleen. Hearing about it the next morning, Alison doesn't know how he accomplished the technical procedure from beginning to end.

Alison is terrified someone will page *her* to the operating room tonight; Mike congratulates himself that no one is cutting on *him* that New Year's Eve.

Residents wander in and out of the room. At 1:00 Mike tells Alison that he wants to leave before the idiots get out on the road. She walks him down through the Emergency Room entrance and watches him enter the gloaming of the wind-whipped parking lot.

It is a quiet evening for her, thank God. She flops into bed hoping to get rid of her headache. She would like to take a shower, but the bathrooms here are disaster areas. Blessedly, no one calls her until a little after 5:00 in the morning. One of the I.C.U. patients is complaining of chest pains. They seem trivial next to her hangover.

Wednesday. 9:00 A.M. The august head of University Hospital's surgical program at City Hospital arrives for his weekly bedside briefing on all University Hospital surgical patients. Dr. Hartwick Abney is a tall and impressive gentleman, tight-lipped, with flinty blue eyes which absorb minute details. Crocodile-belted and gold-buckled over a slight paunch, he wears a buttoned wool vest and a conservatively striped old school tie, and his long white coat is starched and impeccable. His hands are thrust forcefully into his pockets, and curious half-moon specs perch precariously on bristling, graying eyebrows. Dr. Abney is a man who communicates his own importance.

Short-tempered and impatient, he booms thunderbolt questions which require lightning answers, as crisp as his white coat. He can be moved to bellow—in front of colleagues, nurses, patients, anyone—"THAT's not the right answer, YOU DOLT." Invariably the patients are less upset than the residents or medical students. Dr. Abney will plumb their mettle, judgment, and knowledge. In return, he will help edify them with his longer, superior experience and knowledge. Rounds with Dr. Abney is an examination of Mrs. Jones's gangrenous foot or Mrs. Smith's amputated leg. Unfortunately, as time goes on, Mrs. Jones and Mrs. Smith tend to fade into the background of the discussion and rounds will sound like a litany of The Gangrenous Foot or The Amputated Leg.

"You have to guard yourself against forgetting these people have personalities," Alison will say.

The residents and medical students begin to gather in the hall outside the second-floor surgery office, each one greeting Dr. Abney as he or she walks up to join the group.

Without being asked, the women have all worn skirts, looking decidedly a grade more "ladylike" than usual. Kirstin has shed her figure-hugging pants, Carol her tie-dye slacks, Julie her white jeans, and Alison wears a navy blue corduroy skirt and a white blouse with a floppy bow tie her morning coffee narrowly missed. In addition, her dark eyes are carefully outlined with brown-black eyeliner. Everyone has a clean white coat. Everyone has combed his hair.

The flock begins to march uneasily down the hall, with Bernie Schmidt, the chief resident, at Dr. Abney's elbow.

Soft-voiced, Kirstin describes to Julie the reaction of one fifty-four-year-old male patient, scheduled for a hernia repair, whom she recently interviewed in the course of her duties.

"I said 'Have your hernias dropped into your scrotum yet?' and he said 'Oh, no. I don't want anything dropping in there. I'm real active down there.' "

"Your being a girl didn't seem to inhibit him, did it?"

"He said it because I *am* a girl, I think. He told Armstrong, 'Don't let her examine me. I'm a real ladies' man.'

"I will though," says a resolute Kirstin.

The group pauses close to the bed of a forty-three-year-old patient, a wreck of a man with a disturbing history of ten years' addiction to heroin, two years' maintenance on methadone, alcoholism, gall-stones, and pancreatitis. But the immediate problem which brought him into the hospital is a set of vicious stab wounds sustained in his abdomen.

Unlike many of the patients, Mr. Ball does not stare back at this highbrow interest indifferently. His eyes shine with hostility. He may hurl insults at the residents, calling them "you whitey doctors," accusing them of experimenting with his body. He feels he is being killed by all this medical attention.

In City Hospital, life is a struggle both for the patients and the doctors.

Mr. Ball pulls his sheet protectively up to his chin. The physicians discuss what kind of tube to insert through the abdominal wall to drain the operating field after surgery.

Dr. Abney rocks back and forth on his heels. "I've always been death on hard rubber tubes in the peritoneal cavity. Just because Joe Blow in Brooklyn says so, doesn't mean you do it," he opines. "The tube is an extra hazard to the patient."

"How much bowel drainage are you getting?" he asks Bernie Schmidt. "What was the quality of your X-rays on the patient? Terrible? That's ridiculous. Remind me to leave a note to Kate. That's important."

"Dr. Abney refuses to think there could be anything wrong with this hospital," whispers Alison in the hall, as Abney and his nervous following stride to another bedside.

Stopping in front of a cheery, chubby, middle-aged woman sitting comfortably in a chair, Dr. Abney is told that she has gallstones and is due to have her gallbladder removed.

"Is she all right?" Dr. Abney points a finger toward the woman sitting noiselessly in her pink terry bathrobe. It is unusual for him to address a patient directly. Like juggled balls, he throws questions directly to the residents or medical students, while the medical case is exposed clinically in front of the person discussed.

Unfortunately the patient in the pink bathrobe hears her cue for a personal description of her symptoms, and a flow of nonessential information issues forth.

Giggle. Giggle. Gallstones. She knew there was something wrong with her because she bought a girdle "but it just kept rolling down."

"You do what you want," Abney tells her in an attempt to be charming. "You don't pay attention to these doctors." He looks slightly ill at ease. He wants to press on with rounds. How do you bow out gracefully without being rude? No time for this. No time for extraneous chitchat with the patients. Rounds are a ritual for the benefit and edification of the residents and medical students primarily, not the patients.

Dave Fayard looks more and more upset. The woman is his patient. Maybe Dr. Fayard is "losing" a gallbladder.

"If you have gallstones, let them do it," Dr. Abney advises her. He hurries out of the room, his entourage following on his heels in close formation.

Next, Alison "presents" Loretta Rider, standing alone by the woman's bedside while the bulk of the audience bunches shoulder-to-shoulder at the foot of the bed. "In operation, she was found to have a mitotic lesion of the pancreas which has metastasized to the liver." Alison describes the technical surgical procedure, detailing the case as scientifically as possible.

"What else did you do?" Dr. Abney interrupts.

"We did a biopsy."

"Did you do a gastrojejunostomy?"

Bernie Schmidt butts into the interrogation. "Fifteen to twenty-five percent of the patients will have an intestinal obstruction." Anything done or not done in the operating room reflects Schmidt's own supervisory judgment.

"You can look at it another way," Dr. Abney suggests, playing the devil's advocate. "Seventy-five percent will never get into any trouble."

"There was no evidence of deformity of the duodenum from the tumor. We decided that a gastrojejunostomy would only add extra risk," Bernie explains. The procedure would create a surgical connection between the stomach and the duodenum.

Dr. Abney relaxes his tone. "I'm like Bernie. I practically never do it."

"Dave and Bernie will always defend their position or their decision to operate," Alison explains later. But once Alison's chief resident at another hospital backed down under fire by keeping his mouth shut. A question came up at rounds as to whose decision it was to operate and why it was necessary. The chief resident never spoke up. "I couldn't do anything but defend myself very poorly," remembers Alison with disgust. "The chief resident was already pretty low in the residents' esteem and it wasn't hard for him to sink even further after that."

"DR. CARSE!" Dr. Abney's voice lashes sternly across the room. "I'd like you in here!" Both Carol and John Kirke have been talking quietly just outside the doorway to the patients' room, hanging on to the tail end of the group, since the small bedroom is already overly crowded.

John is ignored for the moment.

"One thing I won't go for is a double conference," Dr. Abney reprimands. "Mandatory. If you are here, you participate in the conversation. Otherwise you go someplace else to have a conversation. I don't care. I'm liberal."

Stepping close to the center of the room, Carol smiles more good-naturedly than sheepishly. She is not going to be squelched and she refuses to be upset.

John lingers on the periphery of the group. "He's very good at hiding behind the pole," Alison will say.

Dr. Abney looks at Mrs. Kane, resting indifferently with both legs on the bed, and focuses on her amputated stump.

"Everybody's foot blanches when they raise it, but hers blanches abnormally," he explains to his rapt covey. "A diabetic lacks normal circulation in the extremities." Mrs. Kane is a diabetic.

Eying Carol Carse, Dr. Abney asks, "In the diabetic foot, what are the classical clinical features of an infection?"

Mrs. Kane stares back blankly at the group.

Carol is composed. She thinks hard for a moment, concentrating but unruffled.

"Redness." She thinks a second longer. "Increased heat."

"Is that classical for the diabetic foot? No." His answers collide with his questions.

"Are these clinical signs absolute? Yes. Absolute. Mandatory. Almost absolute. If you don't find it, is it fair to say there's no infection? No, it's not," he says condescendingly. "Why isn't it?"

"Infection in the diabetic is often dormant," replies Carol smoothly. "Particularly in the diabetic."

"That's right," snaps Dr. Abney. "It's not the same as in the well-vascularized person."

Dr. Abney's barrage follows from patient to patient like a peppering of buckshot.

"What was his white blood count?"

"What was her amylase?"

"What was your baseline?"

"What were the indications for an exploration?"

"Can you make a case for antibiotics?"

They discuss a recent journal article on the difference between pig-lung heparin and pig-intestine heparin, used in the treatment of postoperative pulmonary embolism. "Look at the bottle," he warns them, "know which one you are using."

"Quick now," Dr. Abney barks at John, whom he has asked to present a patient. "Quick and precise and to the point."

Mrs. Parks is the next patient whose treatment will be reviewed, and Dr. Abney asks Carol to do the honors. "Go up there," he tells her. "What was your differential diagnosis upon admission? What was your working diagnosis?"

A scared Mrs. Parks recently underwent an exploratory laparotomy and the lysis, or loosening, of adhesions from previous surgery, a hysterectomy for cancer some time ago. Fortunately, the surgical team found no further spread of the cancer.

Now Alison presents Sam Ferguson. She opens with, "Mr. Ferguson is in his eleventh day post-op. He sustained several gunshot wounds, one to the left sternal border in the upper left quadrant." Alison gestures to her chest.

Schmidt interrupts her. "If you're going to point, point correctly. You're pointing to your right scapula when you're talking about your left."

Alison goes on to explain another bullet's damage to Ferguson's intestinal tract and spinal column.

"It's not clear whether he has spinal shock or whether the damage is anatomical," she concludes.

At the end of her discourse, Abney shoots his question to the general group. "What if there is a sympathectomy? Would he feel visceral distension? Where is the student? Have you looked up the problem? What knocks out the visceral pain, and do you think this has happened to this patient?"

Hanging onto every word, Sam Ferguson scowls, trying to decipher the rarefied vocabulary swimming around him, hoping to glean precious nuggets of information as to his true condition.

Dr. Abney looks at Alison.

Alison shakes her head.

Dr. Abney looks at Dave.

Fayard shakes his head.

"Good God, you people!" Dr. Abney protests, his tone reeking disgust.

To Carol he says, "You should read more. You didn't look it up either."

"All right, Bernie, you always know the answer. You tell 'em."

Abney listens to Bernie's exposition and declaims, "That's my answer, too. All right."

Bernie even laughs, a little relieved. His attitude visibly changes with Dr. Abney's compliment. For the past few days, he has been on edge, quick to criticize, quick to find fault, worried that Dr. Abney might publicly reprimand and question his handling of Mr. Lincoln. Now he relaxes noticeably.

"He might not have a complete transection," suggests Dr. Abney.

It is doubtful whether Ferguson understands the panoply of polysyllabic medical words, and the enormity of the medical discussion at his bedside. They may as well be conducting rounds in Urdu.

Turning to Carol, Dr. Abney asks, "What is the status of the patient's parasympathetic nervous system?"

Carol is at a loss.

Dr. Abney bawls impatiently, "You have *days* to think about this!"

Of Julie he demands the name of an arterial branching in the sacrum. "Right," he says, listening to her answer. "Top of the class."

"I argue that a sympathectomy may have left him in a temporarily dysfunctional state. What temperature is he running? 102°? He has a urinary tract infection? No, you're not sure about that," he says contemptuously when no one volunteers an instantaneous reply. "He has a catheter in, right? You're worried that he may be running an infection, right?"

He is coldly and formally polite.

To Schmidt he says, without stopping for breath, "You go to the books and see what a sympathectomy does to the temperature."

Dr. Abney is arguing that Ferguson may have suffered nerve damage in the abdomen, rather than intrinsic physiological abdominal injury.

Dr. Abney can, at times, be stunningly benign. A famous story circulates about a resident, Dorothea Richards, who took charge of a man who appeared in the Emergency Room with a heavily bleeding laceration of the lower arm. Trying to stanch the copious flow, she tied the arm's brachial artery, which supplies much of the circulation to the hand.

The day Dr. Abney came in for his weekly rounds, everyone was on pins and needles to see what would happen when this surgical resident presented her case.

"What did you do that for?" he asked, referring to her closing off of the brachial artery.

"I couldn't stop the bleeding."

"Why not?"

"I didn't know where I was. I had left my anatomy book in the car."

That answer went all around the hospital, and Dr. Abney accepted her explanation because residents learn from experience.

The next patient to be scrutinized is Patty Roper, who grins foolishly from his wheelchair. The details of his case escape his disconnected thinking completely. He can't even remember the name of this hospital.

Wilder outlines the man's current history. Sixty-year-old emaciated derelict. Frostbite victim. The police brought him out of an alleyway with a temperature of 103°, probably due to dehydration.

"A psycho," someone whispers.

"Meanwhile we found and repaired an incarcerated, inguinal hernia," Wilder continues matter-of-factly, by way of explaining why Roper is occupying a surgical rather than a nursing home or psychiatric bed.

"The O.R. nurses covered the feet in bags to insure the upper area would be sterile. We forgot to take them off and the bags provided a perfect medium for bacteria to grow. Shortly afterward he spiked a temperature of 102°."

Dr. Abney is disquieted and stiffly shifts his weight from one foot to the other. "What can you do for those heels?"

"I don't know," says Wilder. "Maybe crossflaps." He is referring to a type of skin graft.

"Oh! That will be awfully hard to do. You need a lot of patience for these frostbite victims. Weeks and weeks. The first impulse you have is to cut it all off."

Abney is more and more discomfited by the senior resident's flow of self-confessed mistakes on a patient who needed an excuse for a bed.

Abney wants to hurry up and end the presentation.

They pass on.

Rounds over, the residents and medical students trail back into the hall, silently following Dr. Abney. Alison and the others want to say good-bye to him. By next Wednesday, they will be starting a new rotation. Alison is assigned to a big, new, well-equipped, well-manicured hospital (a private, private hospital, she says), as sharp a contrast as imaginable with City Hospital.

The residents linger a little longer than usual in a tight cluster with

Dr. Abney the straight-backed mountaintop at the epicenter of their attention.

In parting, Dr. Abney discusses the hemlines of their white coats, denoting hospital rank like stripes on an army officer's uniform. Drs. Abney, Schmidt, Fayard, and Wilder all wear an expanse of white which flows impressively below the knee. Everyone else, including the medical students, wears short white jackets.

"I'm for making no distinction," Abney declares. "I don't think it makes much sense."

No one volunteers his or her opinion.

"I don't think you should separate the years of service. It's going to come up at the next medical meeting. Long coats for everybody."

Dr. Abney feels he has exhausted the discussion on dress. He surveys the group and smiles knowingly. "You'll probably be happy to leave this place. You can go to that big suburban hospital and look after all those rich patients. . . . The nurses even stand up. . . . They say 'Sir.' "

"They'd better not," Alison interjects.

Everyone laughs.

# 23

# Last Day at City Hospital

This morning at 7:10, Lance Sutter, age seventy-two, is at peace with the world, sleeping like a baby on his back in his Intensive Care Unit bed, oblivious to bleeping noises, rushing nurses, and Alison Merrill's critical eye. Lance Sutter, she notices, is sleeping without his required oxygen mask, her specific written and verbal order to the I.C.U. nursing staff.

With a partially blocked circulation to his legs, Mr. Sutter couldn't even walk two city blocks. In an operation for vascular reconstruction, his aorta was hooked up to the femoral arteries by means of a white, synthetic, accordion-pleated tube, simulating a blood vessel, in order to carry more blood to his feet. A heavy smoker with chronic bronchitis, Lance Sutter had alarmingly low blood-oxygen levels after the operation. An oxygen mask will help bring up his oxygen to prevent respiratory acidosis, the retention by the body of excess carbon dioxide. This is the second morning in a row that Alison has breezed by his bed on early-morning rounds and discovered Mr. Sutter without his oxygen mask.

"He said he didn't want to keep it on," the nurse tells Alison nonchalantly.

"I said *specifically* he had to have a face mask and I left an order to restrain his arms."

"I'll put a face mask on him," the nurse says, still nonchalantly, refusing to be pushed.

"Would you please?" Alison's tone is suffused with annoyance and disgust.

"The nurses don't care," she fumes to Carol, who is busy drawing morning blood gases from Alison's various patients. Carol already holds two blood-filled tubes. "We get really pissed off if we get called in the middle of the night because the nurses have let some guy pull out his I.V. But if a patient peels off an oxygen mask, the nurse is not required to call the resident, so she didn't bother to ride herd on Lance Sutter. Get it?" Alison, annoyed, tells Carol.

Before surgery, she had reprimanded Lance Sutter for smoking, scolding him with a straight face even though an open pack of mentholated Benson & Hedges bulged in her white jacket pocket. Later, she found he was sneaking into the toilet to smoke on the sly. He probably figured she wouldn't discover him in the men's room. Mr. Sutter will be cured in spite of himself.

John Kirke, the other medical student assigned to Alison's tutelage, never seems to be around. "I don't know if he thinks I'm not a good teacher or what," she says, puzzled.

At 8:00, she launches into her operating schedule.

It is very hard to compress all a patient's vital information in the small blank space provided on a 8½" x 11" paper form. A pithy preoperative diagnosis scrawled on the O.R. sheet states twenty-year-old Tony Fine's reason for lying on the operating table: foreign body in abdominal wall. Innocent enough. Deadpan medical prose. The foreign bodies are wire sutures; wire sutures are holding together Mr. Fine's tough abdominal fascia; his abdomen was crudely slashed open three years ago during a knife fight.

Because he's a wiry man with little fat padding, the sutures are close to his outer skin surface and pierce the skin if he lifts a heavy object. Now that scar tissue provides a natural seal, Alison will attempt to remove the sutures.

Tony Fine raises his shoulders from the O.R. table to squint at his own X-rays posted on the wall view-box. He will be operated on under a local anesthetic and will be fully conscious. Turning his head in all directions, he looks over the boxlike operating room lined with shelves and packages of 000 black braided silk, gut chromic 0, 4-0 prolene. All sterile and neat.

His abdomen is scrubbed until it foams yellow, the excess mopped with a sterile towel, and his body draped. A small screen of drapes in front of his chin hides his direct view of the surgical theater.

Dave Fayard and Alison talk about the problems of mass transit and the state liquor laws.

She looks at the angry pink knobs of scar tissue under the umbilicus. She can trace the jabs of the attack weapon and the slash of the surgical knife by the thin white line across Tony Fine's stomach.

Tracing a midline incision with the scalpel over the old scar, she slices the skin open starting from above the umbilicus down in a vertical line, and then eases the incision open with her fingers.

Fine squeezes his eyes shut in pain, or simulated pain.

The sutures are imbedded deeply into scar tissue. Alison pulls hard, like wrenching wire staples from a wooden crate. Every once in a while she stops to scan the lighted X-rays to pinpoint the sutures' location. She keeps on cutting a little further down, removing the man's inner wirings one by one, plugging holes with four or five stitches, working stitch by stitch. As she tugs, one wire flies across the room and hits the wall. Alison counts eleven sutures in the metal specimen pan, then finds one more. There may be others, but these are all she can find, and their removal should relieve the patient.

Later she dictates her operative findings into a tape. "Approximately twelve wire sutures, some cut and pulled from the wound. Slight infection. Dry dressing applied."

A few minutes later she is on the phone to the chief resident of the university's "medicine" service. Residents commonly shorten "internal medicine" to simply "medicine." Under pressure from Bernie Schmidt to transfer a patient in order to vacate a surgical bed, she tells the resident about a woman who has not undergone surgery but is demonstrating clinical signs of a pulmonary embolism, a "medical" problem.

Alison is doing a lot of talking in order to convince medicine's chief resident. "Basically people with acute medical problems don't get as good care on our surgical floor. I basically don't feel competent and can't give them that kind of care. I get here at 7:00 and nothing is open. Then I go to the O.R., and I can only begin to do things for my patients when I get out."

Now Alison is silent and the medical chief resident is doing the talking, giving his version in no uncertain terms of why he doesn't have to accept the transfer of surgery's patient.

"Maybe I should have Dr. Schmidt talk to you," Alison says in return, not winning the argument.

The chief resident hangs up abruptly and Alison is acutely embarrassed.

Tense and upset, she pages Bernie Schmidt. "Hey, it's me, Alison. The medical chief resident gave me a lot of crap and a line that the patient belongs to you."

". . . Ah, hah . . . ah, huh. I don't know."

Alison says less and less, gets up and paces next to the desk with the phone in her hand. She is more and more uncomfortable. Schmidt has changed his intentions about this particular patient. The fracas over the aborted leave-taking of Edwin Lincoln has left a bad taste in Schmidt's mouth. "Oh, we can leave the patient on the floor," he tells her.

Restraining the urge to express her resentment at this treatment from the chief resident, she inwardly seethes that Schmidt never bothered to tell her about his change of heart. "That's what happens when you are given your own patients to take care of, but not the administrative responsibility at the top. There I am. I feel like a real jackass."

At the nurses' station, Mrs. Greer is scanning patient files. The social worker always seems unflinchingly busy. They talk briefly about Loretta Rider.

"She has thirteen years of alcoholism she admits to," says Mrs. Greer. "Her children are college-educated and so is she. She's intelligent with nothing to aspire to, so she drinks. I haven't worked out her housekeeping yet."

"I don't care how you do it, but we need that bed." Alison is impatient today. It is time Loretta Rider moved on to make room for another patient. "Just get her out of here and make sure she has adequate housekeeping arrangements. We still need the beds."

At lunch in the cafeteria, she engages in conversation with a surgical resident from another service, who is feeling downcast.

"We don't have blood to operate on our elective cancer patients and a dope pusher comes in and he's shot in the belly and we get 25 units of blood," the surgeon, a small fellow from South America, complains. "We fix him up and he is back on the streets. What does it all mean? Sometimes you wonder about the quality of life after surgery. Is it worth it?"

"Or the quality of death," says Alison. Many of the residents wonder, in fact, whether surgery indeed "cures" the patient. The surgery may be just a transient problem of a disordered life-style that produces other, more traumatic problems.

Alison's place as the sole female surgical resident for her year prompts her fellow surgical resident to digress about women in the job world. ''There are some physical jobs that genetically would be very difficult for women to do. Like ditch digging. And I can't figure a woman orthopod.'' Orthopod is hospital jargon for an orthopedic surgeon.

''I saw a female orthopedist at University Hospital,'' says Alison quietly, ''and she was incredibly good and everyone was very impressed.''

''I would like to see her reduce a badly overriding fractured femur with a lot of muscle spasms. I wanted so much to do it once and I couldn't put the bones together. Everyone was laughing at me.

''I think intellectually women are as well prepared,'' he continues. ''But because of genetics they are less suitable for our present society. There are certain things. She is pregnant. She has menstrual periods. She feels lousy. O.K.?'' He feels he has made his point clearly enough. ''I could probably say this a little better in Spanish. I don't think you could be a female neurosurgeon with three or four babies because they would be raised without a mother.''

''Usually they're raised without a father,'' Alison points out softly. It is an easy moment of social conversation. Alison is a good listener, not ruffling any feathers, but not necessarily agreeing with him either.

He backtracks. ''Is it right to have your ego boosted at 5:00 on rounds—'Oh, he's such a good doctor'? Or is it more important to be called a good father?''

At clinic in the afternoon of the last day, Alison examines Rebecca Hanley, who was discharged as an in-hospital patient a few days ago. Rebecca Hanley is still coiled up in a ball and glassy-eyed. She shakily twists her fingers over and over again. Her skin is literally stretched over the bones without intervening muscle fiber. But there is no crying today and she seems more resigned and happier than before.

Although Rebecca Henley is clean and without infection, Alison is surprised at the size of the bedsores on either side of the sacrum. She picks up a clear plastic ruler. Five inches across.

"They're so big, there's no real chance of their ever closing over," comments Alison.

"Hey, Don"—she opens the curtain and calls to Wilder in the hall. "Are these bedsores as big as you remember?"

Don comes over and shrugs. "I saw her a week ago. That is what they looked like."

"O.K. As long as they haven't gotten worse." She wraps a bandage around a quiet Rebecca Hanley's gaping sore.

"Are you all right, sweetie?" Alison shakes her arm. Rebecca Hanley radiates peace. The clinic routine is one she is used to.

A smiling nurse walks up to Alison. "We were asking earlier where is Fan-tas-tic. I hope we can say good-bye to her."

Alison laughs. "That's because I sometimes say '*Faaan*-tastic,' " she explains.

After the nurse leaves, Alison sighs. "I'm so happy to leave this hospital. It's so frustrating. It's worse than most. If the lab does shitty work, Dr. Abney wants *us* to do something about it. He thinks there is nothing wrong with this hospital.

"When something goes wrong with the X-rays, Abney thinks that's outlandish. I have to fight to get the X-rays I want. Getting an X-ray done of the G.I. tract with the help of a dye—you have to negotiate to get that done because the X-ray technician doesn't really want to do it.

"When I go down to X-ray, I bat my eyelashes and flirt a bit and ask for what I want. Then if I don't get it, I get really pissed off. Then when it's done, I'm all feminine again. Thank you so much. And he's willing to accept me again because I'm acting like a woman.

"And this hospital is so crazy you start laughing at anything and everything, and at the wrong times."

The rest of the day is spent completing charts in Hospital Records—a room with rows and rows of manila folders stashed on utility shelving—finishing up the discharge summaries, all the paperwork there wasn't time to do earlier in the week.

As a veteran, Sam Ferguson will be transferred to a veterans' hospital, no questions asked.

Later, upstairs on the surgical floor, Alison spies Ferguson's girlfriend coming in, sad-faced, bringing irises.

Loretta Rider is beginning to look amorphous. Perhaps it is the loss of eye contact. When the flurry of white coats passes by on daily rounds, she doesn't bother to lift her head and look up. Sitting listlessly for long periods of time in the chair next to her hospital bed, she is lost in thought, staring intently at the floor. Dave tells Alison he thinks she will only last a few more months.

In a last Keystone Cops sequence, Alison calls the city police asking what to do with a piece of ''evidence'' for one of their cases: a bullet extracted on admission from Sam Ferguson's split-open flesh. Generally the residents etch their initials on the bullets they dig out, but Alison and Dave don't want to do it this time. They don't want to possibly identify themselves with a potential killer.

''We'll be right over,'' the police say. In a flash, five dumfounded policemen arrive on the floor, confused by Alison's call. They think someone has been shot on the ward. The police call to cancel the oncoming detectives. It turns out there is a special person at City Hospital who routinely receives bullets from gunshot wounds as part of his job.

By the end of a day filled with details, Alison leaves City Hospital for her next rotation without knowing if Sam Ferguson and his fiancée married, if the social dispositions found a home, if Loretta Rider resolved her family problems for the last days of her life, if Brad Foster was able to make a living minus one foot.

A few months later, Alison hear some news concerning Ferguson through another resident then rotating through City Hospital. Despite his threats, the jilted suitor never came in to finish the job. He didn't have to. Ferguson's girlfriend left her paraplegic lover of her own accord.

# 24
# Private, Private


Alison Merrill no longer sets the alarm on her bedside table. It is sheer useless effort. She has ceased to hear its loud, bothersome buzz altogether. The two staggered alarms across the room have become barely perceptible noise. Fortunately, Mike is working a day shift at the Westinghouse plant and rises earlier than he did in the beginning of the year.

"Alison, that was your alarm. Get up."

Shaking Alison's shoulder no longer serves to rouse her. The sound of a shower pounding full-blast is ineffectual.

Mike turns over and puts his feet on her back and shoves. Alison has no awareness that she is being so rudely awakened. Her eyes snap open.

"You've got to go to work and make some money."

Alison leaves the mainstream of commuter traffic and drives her car through a community of tidy single-family homes with basketball hoops poised over two-car garages. Eventually she comes to an impressive horseshoe ramp around islands of greenery dotted with wooden benches, shaded by tall, lush trees, and climbs up the driveway toward a red brick rectangular monolith with smaller subsidiary buildings.

She has spent a partly restless night and only fell into a sound sleep toward morning. She suspects her queasy stomach might be due to a dinner of curried tunafish she concocted at the last minute, the recipe gleaned from a paperback seafood cookbook. She and Mike were suddenly tired of the steady diet of tuna-noodle casserole they have because it is fast, cheap, and easy for Alison to make. She didn't gulp down any breakfast today, and she tries to ignore her mild nausea.

Around noontime, the cars pulling up the ramp to suburban Lakeside Hospital will unload well-dressed passengers, mothers carrying well-bundled babies. Coats will be fur-trimmed, and the passenger vehicles will include an occasional Mercedes. The driver of a white florist van will step out to deliver a basket of greenery and a clear glass bowl filled with fresh fruit and bonbons.

Inside, the lobby is relatively peaceful. Heels sink into inches-thick gray carpeting; visitors refer to bright acrylic directional arrows or a polite receptionist, and walk by freshly painted walls on the way to the bank of elevators.

Some visitors are waiting, staring, reading, or listening to the piped Musak, sitting in deep, soft, bulky red and navy armchairs. Ashtrays are sunk into simulated marble slabs. A loudspeaker occasionally interrupts the dreamy music to ask questions or make announcements: "Is anyone waiting for Sheldon Spitz?" "Wendy Kovaks has reached her room."

"This is one of the hospitals," says Alison, "where the residents get true technical skill in the operating room."

A voice like the others interrupts again, deliberate, cool, soft, singsong: "M-set, Emergency Room, M-set, Emergency Room, M-set, Emergency Room."

M-set is the local hospital code (at City Hospital it was Code Blue) for a respiratory or cardiac arrest, an immediate emergency. Any available doctors near the area mentioned must rush to the announced location.

On a normal day, Alison will push open the door to the anteroom outside the Doctors' Locker Room to pick out a scrub suit from the piles sorted by size on a tall metal rack against the wall.

One time a non-teaching attending surgeon walked into the anteroom before pushing the door to the Doctors' Locker Room and asked, "You're not going to change in here, are you?"

"Sure," she said mischievously. "The sign reads 'Doctors' Locker Room.' It doesn't say anything about a male locker room."

"The flowered caps are here, Dr. Merrill," Jackie Barry, the head nurse, now shouts down the hall.

"Great! I'm happy about that," says Alison.

It is her one attempt to upgrade her dull, everyday scrub attire. "I think they fit better instead of ballooning out in back like the standard nurses' caps. The flowered ones tie in the back and are comfortable and more flattering." Some of the nurses make their own caps, with a dress to match, in any bright print that meets their fancy. "It's not that I couldn't do it," Alison says. "I used to make my own outfits in high school. But Mike would object to doing another load of laundry."

Alison takes the scrubs a short distance to the female locker room and sheds her khaki culotte skirt and bright plaid shirt. *True Story* and other magazines for the lovelorn are scattered about, with articles such as "A Woman's Guide to Love and Marriage" or "My Son or My Lover, I Can't Keep Both."

Twenty-five minutes later she is in the sparkling operating room positioning clamps to hold open the edges of a breast skin flap for a radical mastectomy. Today Alison scrubs with Dr. Spencer Mills, a middle-aged, tall, outspoken surgical attending with eyebrows that move up and down like elevators and an impish twinkle in his eyes.

Private attendings have their own private practices and their own private patients. Entitled to admitting privileges at Lakeside, the attendings are authorized to operate and treat patients inside Lakeside Hospital's walls with the assistance of the hospital staff. Some of them, called "teaching attendings," have elected while treating their patients to teach residents and interns in the practical atmosphere of the hospital. In return, the residents attend to the patients in their absence. For instance, if the condition of a teaching attending's patient begins to deteriorate at night while the attending is away, the resident is the first person to be called; the resident would in turn alert the attending.

"You make sure the patient lives through the night," Alison will sometimes crack, "while the attending is sleeping."

The atmosphere of Lakeside's spic-and-span, spit-and-polish operating room is that of martial discipline enclosed within the hushed, reverent tones proper for a cathedral. Cursing at the nurses, throwing instruments on the floor, is not tolerated here. Misdemeanors are reported and the offender is treated to a royal dressing-down by the nursing supervisor of the O.R. staff. The surgeon commands, and the nurse harkens.

Mrs. Bernstein, the forty-seven-year-old woman on the operating table, has a large growth in her right breast which is dimpling her skin. The suggestion of cancer is strong, and a frozen section confirms the suspicion. The surgical team proceeds with their radical mastectomy. Alison holds a square white laparotomy sponge over the breast, rolling and pulling the sponge against the breast tissue to give traction while Dr. Mills cuts around the inframammary fold. The surgical precision proceeds smoothly, while some of the cutting is reserved for the conversation, laced with teasing jabs and barbs.

"See how women fuss and fight over everything," Dr. Mills tells Alison and the entourage of nurses in mock anger.

"They'll slow you up every time," says Alison, matching wit for wit.

A nurse counts the 4" x 4" gauze sponges midway through the operation. "Sponge count is correct, sir."

"To be fair," says Dr. Mills, "men can sew at least as well as the ladies."

And during a slight tiff over the direction of the skin stitches: "See how women interfere with medicine. I guess you have to be pretty fair to all the minority groups. They're very well intentioned, but really not too able."

Then he teases the scrub nurse: "A good scrub nurse should have three hands."

"There's an Indian deity that would do very well," answers the circulating nurse.

"The one with seven arms? That woman would scare me to death."

"Actually, that reminds me of a lot of men I've met," says Alison.

The circulating nurse laughs. "Dr. Merrill gets passing marks all day."

Removing the drapes from the patient in order to bandage her chest, Dr. Mills throws the bloodstained sheets unceremoniously on the floor to get them out of his way quickly.

Bending down to pick up the messy pile, the circulating nurse pretends to protest. "Women in medicine don't throw things on the floor like men in medicine. Geeeeee!"

"O.K.," says Dr. Mills, accepting any repartee as a matter of due course, "let's sit her up."

Propping up Mrs. Bernstein, Alison and Dr. Mills circle layer after layer of Ace bandage around her chest.

"Give her plasma through the I.V.," he instructs Alison. "We encourage them to use their arm from the very first day."

A short time later in the recovery room, where patients reorder their confused senses, a nurse asks Alison whether she is going to tell Mrs. Bernstein about the loss of one of her breasts.

"I've never even *met* the lady," Alison argues defensively. "Doesn't Dr. Mills normally tell his patients?"

"Someone has to tell her, and Dr. Mills didn't wait for her to come out of the anesthesia."

"Residents don't like to do it and the anesthesiologists won't," Alison grumbles. "It's an awkward situation."

"The only alternative," suggests the recovery room nurse, "is to send her to her room and have her husband tell her."

"That's not too good," declares Alison.

"Dr. Mills saw the husband as he went out the door and he knows."

Alison decides to check with Dr. Mills himself by asking the hospital operator to page him. "Hi! Hate to bother you. Recovery said you didn't say anything to Mrs. Bernstein. Do you want me to say anything before she's sent up to her room?

". . . O.K. . . . I'll tell her," Alison replies.

Stretched out stiffly, a blonde Mrs. Bernstein holds her hand to her forehead as if suffering from a massive headache, as if it is too painful to open her eyes.

Alison leans over the cold metal bed rail. "The operation went well." She pauses to make sure the woman hears her. "We found more than we expected. We did a mastectomy."

"Oh, I figured you did. Well, that's life." No tears as yet.

Walking away from Mrs. Bernstein's side toward the door, the nurse comes up to Alison before she leaves. "Thank you very much, Dr. Merrill," she says gratefully.

"I didn't feel that a stranger should tell Mrs. Bernstein," explains Alison, now heading down a hospital corridor, "but Dr. Mills asked me to do it and I had no choice. I would be more forward with a patient who knew my face and with whom I had rapport.

"Some of the attendings don't want you to interfere with their relationship to their patients, and then you can't let a patient think you know a thing. The patients ask the resident, 'Well, what did I have? What did you find during my operation?' You feel like such a fool to have to say that you don't know yet.

"I had one patient who had a large pelvic mass. There was a 99 percent chance that it was cancer. She had a biopsy done of the tumor and I purposely didn't read the pathology report so that I could go in there and say in all honesty that I didn't know the result of the lab tests. I used to hate to go to talk to her every morning until I knew that she had been told she had cancer. It turned out that she had known all along from her doctor that she had a malignancy and she was desperately looking for someone to tell her the results were good, to contradict the alarming news her own doctor had told her.''

In a working section of the staff lounge, Dr. Mills has already dictated his operative report into a Tele-Tone Dictation System with cassettes that are changed automatically. He is now wearing a heavy blue silk suit and a navy blue tie on which are embroidered tennis rackets. The walls of the lounge are egg yolk and turquoise, and the surgeons relax on a cushioned black-and-white couch and soft gray chairs. The physicians here look affluent and debonair, sartorially splendid with fashionable wide cravats and crocodile moccasins. And even in baggy scrubs, these surgeons manage to look distinguished. A morning newspaper and a few weighty surgical journals are strewn around the room. An enormous percolator of lukewarm, slightly stale coffee sits on a low round coffee table next to a pile of styrofoam cups, sugar, Sweet'n Low, and a jar of Coffee-mate.

One surgeon is writing on an index card. "What are these numbers?" he puzzles out loud. "Oh! This is my golf score."

Dr. Mills relaxes, too, and watches Alison sit down and take out a mentholated cigarette for a quick puff before the next case.

"I talked my daughter out of medicine," he says, passing the time. "She was interested in a social career." He sweeps a hand up to the ceiling. "It's not nice to say about your daughter, but with her flight into society, she would never have kept her nose in a book."

"I don't know. I certainly goofed off at times in medical school."

"She's completed one year of nursing school. That's much better for her. Next year she's getting married. He's going to law school and she'll be able to support him."

"Women in medicine are fine as long as they are home in time to cook dinner," volunteers an older surgeon across the room, a cup of coffee in one hand, a cigarette in the other.

"I've convinced my son to come into medicine," continues Dr. Mills. "At first I played the devil's advocate and asked him why. He said, 'Because a lot more lawyers than doctors are being graduated. There's less competition. You're your own boss, you have prestige, and you can make plenty of money.' ''

Alison, getting up from her chair: "That's not true now."

Dr. Mills nods pensively. "Yes, the doctor doesn't have half the prestige he had twenty or thirty years ago. A recent poll showed that doctors were one step above garbage collectors."

A nurse scurries into the staff lounge in a flurry. "The boy's already asleep and the anesthesiologist is jumping up and down." The nurse is looking desperately for the surgeon, Dr. Tom Laramy, whose young patient is already anesthetized on the operating room table.

A short, portly doctor with bushy gray sideburns rushes down the hall and disappears into the Doctors' Locker Room.

An eight-year-old boy suffering from congenital spherocytosis, a hereditary blood disease, is scheduled for a splenectomy. His spleen, now abnormally swollen, is sequestering red blood cells.

"There's no way Jeremy Kohler is going to do me out of this kid," says Alison before stepping into the operating room. Her chief resident wants to assist in the surgery, but Alison will not be pushed from the operating room table by reason of seniority.

The surgical team includes Dr. Laramy, Jerry Kohler, Alison, and John Peltzer, a medical student. Dr. Laramy's surgical work is neat and tidy. Every vessel is properly and carefully clamped, tied, and sutured with minimal blood loss. He goes under the spleen to "tie" the splenic artery first, a technique he has recently learned at a surgical seminar in Michigan.

"After a while," says a scrub nurse, "you can just predict what instruments a surgeon will ask for. Dr. Mills asks for a Kelly, a long, heavy hemostat used to pinch closed bleeding blood vessels during surgery. When he operates, it will sound like a constant stream of demands for 'Kelly! Kelly! Kelly!' Another surgeon, Dr. Cecil Towers, uses an unusual number of mini-mosquitoes, the smallest kind of hemostat. Cell dissection is what we nurses call his technique. The attendings differ about dressings as well as instruments and the post-op care of the patient, including details of diet and when exactly to pull the I.V. You can even tell when two surgeons have trained in the same hospital."

In the operating room, Dr. Laramy wants a kickbucket beside his right foot.

"Some people go to famous places, like Minnesota's Mayo Clinic, to be operated on. Here they come to me, not the hospital," declares Dr. Laramy. "It's my responsibility to see they are operated on and treated my way. Should you treat the tissues with delicacy or charge into the surgery with utmost speed? Treating the tissues delicately is important in any operation. The amount of shock often has to do with delicacy of handling.''

He is annoyed with the scrub nurse for the paucity of mini-mosquitoes allotted to him on the instrument table. ''I want to feel that delicacy. If I want to clamp a vessel, I want to clamp the vessel and not the fat with it. Next time if we don't have enough, let me know. I have some of my own.''

In a short time, Dr. Laramy is again annoyed, because he does not spot a sufficient number of regular-sized hemostats on the instrument table. ''Are we short of hemostats, too?''

''Yes,'' answers the scrub nurse meekly.

''What does my card say?'' Index cards are filed on all the surgeons, noting their likes and dislikes in surgical apparatus.

Many surgical instruments are named after surgeons—Kelly, Balfour, Richardson, DeBakey, Babcock—like mountains after heads of state.

''It says to have them, sir.''

''Will you please send Jackie in here.''

The head surgical nurse, Jackie Barry, is successfully paged to come into the O.R. An older, serious woman with glasses, she publicly professes innocence. ''If they're not here and if they're not upstairs, I don't know where they are.''

''Don't you think someone in the hospital should know? What does my card say?'' he reiterates.

''That's what I'll try to find out.'' She leaves without seeming flustered.

Alison knows why Dr. Laramy is upset. Dr. Towers is operating next door and is using a goodly number of mini-mosquitoes.

A nurse drops in to borrow some retractors. The scrub nurse won't allow it.

Later, another nurse comes in pleading, hands folded in supplication, for an extra armboard, an extension of the operating table which supports the patient's outstretched arms. Exiting, she skips and throws a kiss in thanks, the armboard tucked like a trophy under her arm.

The operation is two hours long. ''I know why I'm tired,'' Dr. Laramy tells Alison. ''You have the table at your height.''

"I'm sorry," apologizes Alison. Turning to the circulating nurse, she asks, "Do you want to raise the table for Dr. Laramy?"

Dr. Laramy is worried he is holding up another surgeon scheduled for the operating room right after his case. "Has Dr. Busch been moved to another operating room? I'd like to know, because if he has, then I don't feel as pressed for time and I can go discharge my patients."

The circulating nurse comes back into the operating room. "Dr. Laramy, I talked to Jackie. She said not to worry, because Dr. Busch is still in his office."

With the operation nearly complete, Dr. Laramy will turn over the routine skin closure to his younger assistants.

He leaves to discharge two patients who are waiting for him in their rooms. Alison, holding forceps in one hand and a curved needle with suture clamped in a needle holder in the other, teaches the medical student how to put in the skin stitches. The skin closing is taking much longer, of course, but the nurses are taking it gracefully.

"You're a good teacher," the scrub nurse tells Alison.

"Teaching is an important part of the work in any medical school-affiliated hospital," Alison will say later. "Sometimes you force yourself to do it. It's really hard to sit back and let someone else take over, when I know it would take me half the time."

Dr. Laramy rushes into the O.R. for a quick moment.

"Alison, I'm not quite happy with the skin closure. The skin should be closed but with the edges barely touching."

"O.K."

Complaining that the skin stitches are too tightly knotted and too crooked, which might leave unsightly puckers when swelling subsides, he wants the stitches to sit comfortably, parallel and evenly spaced.

"Just think of how you would want to look. Although this patient is a boy, remember that with a girl you have to be particularly careful. If the skin wrinkles when edema set in, which always happens, the skin is going to be left hanging."

After Dr. Laramy leaves, John Peltzer stares wide-eyed and open-mouthed across the stretched-out, anesthetized body at Alison. "You should have told him that I was closing."

"It's still my responsibility."

# 25
# How the Dairy Queen Got Pregnant

"What do you want, honey?" says a fifty-five-year-old, good-looking man, gray and mustachioed, stretching languidly in bed. He gazes at Alison through sleepy, heavy-lidded, soft brown eyes.

"You want it, I've got it," he drawls flirtatiously with the trace of a southern accent.

Lifting his arm from behind his head, he reaches out to hold her hand and studies her for a moment. "You sure are prettier than those other doctors."

Like Bo Peep leading her sheep, Alison is making rounds with two medical students in tow, Thayer Davey and John Peltzer, checking on the private patients to whom she is assigned as the private attendings' resident.

"How are you doing?" Alison asks.

"Why do you ask?"

"Well, you know more than I do," she says casually.

"I didn't ask what are you looking for, I said you were looking good today." He holds on to her hand.

Mr. Harris, the old fox, doesn't seem to know what has happened to him under the knife in the operating room. Perhaps to prolong the conversation, he asks mildly for an explanation. Why is he taking insulin, he wants to know. Didn't they take out his gallstones?

Alison doesn't specify that the surgical team, of which she was one pair of hands, found an apricot-sized cancer on the head of the pancreas. "We took out your spleen and pancreas and hooked up your bile duct to the bowel. The gallbladder was one of the things we *didn't* take out." He shakes his head disbelievingly.

She finishes with the suggestion that "there are some surgical cures for the disease." Purposely, Alison uses a euphemistic term for the word "cancer."

The two medical students, sallow and stoop-shouldered, stand there, arms crossed, and watch.

If he didn't want to know anything about his ailment, he wouldn't have asked, Alison feels. The old theory was that you lied to the patient: "Oh, no! You don't have cancer." People are more aware now. Feeling bad for him, Alison tries to lighten the subject.

"You told us a joke before you were operated on. Do you feel good enough to tell us that same joke?" she prompts him.

The charming codger has life in him yet. "Oh," he says innocently, "the one about the Dairy Queen?"

Alison nods.

"Do you know how the Dairy Queen got pregnant?"

He pauses suspensefully, and rolls his eyes at Alison. "The Burger King forgot to put a wrapper on his whopper."

The medical students stifle a guffaw. Alison has heard this one before and smiles quietly.

Mr. Harris pats her bottom. She doesn't flinch. She guesses that Mr. Harris is trying to get his mind off the possibility of a more serious problem the surgeons may have discovered under the knife.

But he is only warming up to his repertoire of off-color jokes. "Do you know the one about the one-hundred-year-old woman? All these people came to her birthday party and congratulated her. You've never been sick, they asked. No. You've never been bedridden? Oh, I've been bedridden plenty and once in a buggy."

The group takes their leave, sniggering, and out of earshot in the hall Alison huffs with irritation. "You're really in a bind when a patient asks you for specifics. I can't lie to him. I can't say that I was in the operating room but I don't know what went on. The attending will get mad at me for telling him. Just what am I supposed to do in a situation like that?"

They walk toward the next patient's room at the end of the hall, passing the glassed-in waiting room. "The attendings all have different ways of handling the patients. You have to find out fast," she says describing her role with saving irony. "Some surgeons want to be called up immediately if their patient turns over in bed. If another patient has a cardiac arrest, that surgeon wants to know about it the next morning.

"One attending blew up at me because I sent his patient to the I.C.U. after a cardiac arrest. The surgeon was away for the weekend and the answering service took a while to get through to him. But I wasn't going to wait around to hear from him. Later he said, 'Why did you send my patient to the I.C.U. without my permission?' I told him, 'Gee, I thought an M-set was an indication for the I.C.U.' To begin with, he was probably angry he didn't hear immediately one of his patients had arrested, and there was a foul-up with the guy who was covering for him.

"And always write out your own order," she admonishes the medical students. "One time I agreed with the attending's order on the chart, so I simply wrote 'As above' and the attending thought I hadn't been there to check on his patients. Now, if the patient has improved slightly, and the attending has asked the nurses for vital signs four times a day, 'V.S. Q.I.D.,' I'll write: ' V.S. T.I.D.' " Translated, this means decrease vital signs to three times a day.

"You call one of the attendings and say I'm admitting one of your patients, who has XYZ, and tomorrow he had *better* have XYZ. You can't diagnose an appy and find out the next morning the guy's vomiting because he's been drinking." Appy is resident slang for an appendectomy.

"Usually you would give an enema to a patient before a hemorrhoidectomy. But Dr. Mills, for one, doesn't want a pre-op enema because he wants the anal sphincter dilated by a normal stool as soon as possible after surgery.

"In the operating room, there are physicians you know you can be late for. Laramy never starts his cases on time. Towers starts fifteen minutes early.

"Your relationship with the attendings runs a lot more smoothly if you pay attention to their particular way of doing things. Basically, the medical politics are: If you've been a good little girl, you'll end up doing my appendectomy."

Next, introducing herself as Dr. Busch's resident, she passes her stethoscope over the abdomen of a patient who has had his gallbladder removed. Mr. Leeds, grimacing and thin, patiently follows her instructions to sit up and breathe in and out. She and the medical students change the dressing over his incision, spreading a towel-like abdominal pad to soak up excess drainage, and some 4″ x 4″ gauze sponges.

She gives the dirty dressing to John Peltzer to discard. "Medical students clean up the mess," he groans.

"Are you passing any gas, Mr. Leeds?" she asks matter-of-factly.

Mr. Leeds looks uncomprehending.

"Any wind?"

Thayer Davey mutters to Alison under his breath, "Ask him if he's farting."

Back in the hall, Alison shakes her head and reproaches the medical student. "Patients, the uneducated ones, don't like you to talk down to them. If you say 'Did you piss?' instead of 'Are you urinating?' they're very insulted. You come at it a different way: 'Did you pass water?' "

At the nurses' station on 8 West, surrounded by white cupboards and white formica desk tops, Alison spots Dr. Glenn Stedman, Mr. Harris' surgeon. Leafing through a patient's buttercup yellow folder, with a matching buttercup yellow push-button phone at his elbow, he leans comfortably and elegantly into his chair as if he had all the leisure in the world. A trim-looking man, he wears white buck moccasins, striped trousers, a light blue shirt with small white polka dots, a navy blue blazer, and a heavy gold watch. Alison stands next to his chair while he gazes up at her impassively.

"Mr. Harris asked why he was on insulin," Alison tells Dr. Stedman, bringing him up to date. "I said in so many words that he was going to be on insulin for the rest of his life because we took out his pancreas. Do you want me to tell him anything else?"

"His wife knows it in every detail," says Dr. Stedman, exasperated. "He doesn't really want to know."

"I told him we took out a tumor without specifically telling him it was cancer."

" 'Growth' would have been better," he replies, icily.

"If they ask," Dr. Stedman instructs Alison, "if they try to con the resident, you say you haven't read the Path report." He shrugs petulantly.

Alison wonders if Dr. Stedman is one of the old-fashioned doctors who thinks it is not the patient's right to know his entire medico-surgical problem.

"For medical students the really good rounds are the teaching rounds at City Hospital," John Peltzer claims. "Private patients would object to being used as teaching models."

Walking through long, winding wings, they reach the pediatric floor in a new building. A pink-uniformed nurse cradles a wee tot at the nurses' station, aglow in white and pumpkin, while another child sways to and fro in a Swyngomatic. A small boy reaches up from his wheeled stretcher to push the elevator button.

A mother pulls two little girls down the hall for a short ride in a bright red playwagon. The children's hospital gowns are blue with a motif of toys.

A Charlie Chaplin figure, toy soldiers, and "Love" and "Smile" signs alternate and march down the hall swinging from strings attached to the ceiling.

Jeffrey Fix, the eight-year-old boy whose spleen was removed earlier in the day, lies on his back in his room, sleeping. He opens his eyes dazedly as the small group making rounds walks in.

His attractive, thirtyish mother, with long auburn hair and heavy mascara, sits very straight at his bedside, her hands folded and calm in her lap. She looks up and smiles sweetly at Alison.

"Have you been up?" Alison asks Jeffrey.

"He ended up sleeping all the time," says his mother.

"You'd better get up soon."

With the willing help of the mother, Alison sits up a resistive patient to listen to his chest.

Afterward, Alison gives Jeffrey some special instructions. "This is going to sound very mean, but if you want to get out of the hospital and start eating again, you have to walk at least four times a day. You're going to have to force it. . . . How are you feeling?"

"Fine," he says in a very small thin voice, moving his head groggily on the pillow and answering almost automatically. "I want a drink of water."

"No, not until tomorrow."

"YES!" He screws up his face into a series of tight wrinkles and starts to cry.

"Not even any dinner?" asks Jeff pleadingly, even more thinly.

"No."

"Nooooo," he protests, disappointed. "I want dinner."

Alison reaches up and fingers the I.V. tubing, through which a mixture of dextrose and water are sliding quietly into the boy from an upside-down bottle on the metal intravenous pole. "You're getting hamburger and French fries through here."

Alison turns to the mother and tells her that she can leave orders for ice chips to moisten the boy's mouth and relieve some of his impression of thirst.

Then Alison glances back at Jeff. "You have to promise to spit it out," she says firmly. "Does that sound like a fair deal?"

"NO!" counters Jeff in a whiny voice, shutting his eyes.

"You have to spit it out, Jeffrey," the mother reminds him.

"I'll drink it. Ooooooh! My stomach. It hurts."

"After surgery, there is no peristalsis for a couple of days," Alison explains to the mother, to warn her intelligently of the danger of letting her son swallow water. "The bowel was handled, and if we let him eat and drink, his stomach will distend and he'll vomit and might pop his stitches."

The mother argues quietly with her child as they leave.

In a sunny room where a stuffed Bugs Bunny occupies the corner of a steel-railed crib, a young woman with long blonde hair, a blue hospital gown, and gloves is sitting in an armchair near the window, giving a bottle to a diapered one-and-a-half-year-old boy. The woman's mask has slipped down around her neck.

"Are you the mother?" Alison asks the woman.

"No, I'm Robin Snell, the nurse."

The boy's shoulder, right arm, right breast, forehead, and part of his back are lobster red. The grossly pockmarked skin is missing in splotches, or sloughing off.

The plump baby sits on the nurse's lap, the only child in a large room. Alison listens to his chest with her stethoscope and the nurse tries to calm him with a bottle. A tray of untouched scrambled eggs and bacon and barely touched corn flakes sits on the floor.

The boy has second-degree burns over 20 percent of his body acquired by tipping over a pot of beans boiling atop a stove. He can't lean back because the fried patch on his back hurts too much.

"He was in so much pain, it took four people to hold him down in the Emergency Room. The mother was totally guilt-ridden and refused to consider that the child might die. She wouldn't look at him in the E.R. or accompany him to the floor.'' Alison talks with some disgust in her voice. ''It turns out that she had a little sister who was badly burned and who died at Lakeside about ten years ago.''

The boy whines and cries softly as Alison, in gown, gloves, mask, and paper shoe covers taken from a special cart parked outside the boy's room, proceeds to examine his burns.

''Hi, sweetie,'' Alison coos to the baby.

He is referred to by the residents simply as ''The Burn Baby.'' In protective isolation, he is being guarded against the outside environment. The skin provides a natural barrier. Any kind of break in the skin provides a ripe opportunity for bacterial invasion and infection. Later, the surgeons can begin to consider skin grafts.

''Have you noticed a cough?'' Alison asks Robin Snell.

The nurse shakes her head.

The baby starts to cry again.

''I can turn on 'Sesame Street,' '' Robin Snell says to him in the soothing singsong tone adults use with children. ''Do you want to hear 'Sesame Street'?''

The baby holds his bottle and bites on the nipple as if he were teething, looking distrustfully at Alison.

Alison tries to stretch his arm and he screams in pain. ''Can't. Can't.''

''May I have a gauze to cover his eyes?'' asks the nurse. Alison obliges, also pulling up the nurse's gown, unbuttoned in back, which is hanging down, exposing her blouse.

''Can you pull up the mask, too?'' asks the nurse, and Alison does so.

While the nurse tries to hold a square piece of gauze over the baby's eyes, Alison begins to spray Betadine over the burns to ward off infection. The liquid drips down in brown-yellow globules.

''No, no, no, no!'' yells the boy, squirming.

The nurse's mask falls down again.

''What a bunch of old meanies we are,'' says Alison. She sprays the arm directly.

''Dirty, dirty,'' he objects, looking down at his yellow-brown body.

Alison rubs the sole of his foot gently. He looks at her and screams.

Picking him up, she tries to comfort him as the nurse changes her stained gown. The hefty boy looks enormous in Alison's arms.

"He's keeping his arm fairly well spiked," Alison comments, peering at the boy's rigidly bent and burned elbow. She is worried the arm may scar and set in a flexion contracture.

"He does straighten his arm when he wants to," says the nurse, taking the child back in her arms. "He drew out his arm when his mother came."

Walking down the floor to the Pediatric Intensive Care Unit, Alison seeks out the head pediatric nurse. A tall, dark woman with neatly cropped hair holds a small four-year-old boy who is vomiting. The most striking characteristic about Sue Donato is the no-nonsense air of authority about her. She is about thirty-five, almost ten years Alison's senior.

Concerned that while The Burn Baby is being fondled, fed, and held his open sores may be brushing against the nurses' hair, creating the spark for infection, Alison asks if the nurses could wear surgical caps to enclose their hair.

Lifting the vomiting child into another nurse's arms, Sue Donato is immediately defensive. "It's not routine," she declares, assessing Alison intently. "All the nurses around here are clean." Alison winces slightly. Her concern was for the baby. She was not implying any slovenliness on the part of the nursing staff.

Sue Donato looks unsmilingly and unblinkingly at Alison. "Personally, I don't see the point of caps. There are wisps of hair which come out of the caps. In any case, he plays on the floor."

Visibly shocked, Alison is open-mouthed. She laughs once, with a half grunt of astonishment. The child is almost certainly courting infection on a scuffed floor.

"I don't know what the status of the laundry is here," says Alison, "but I would like to see him playing on a sterile sheet."

"We'd have to order more of them specially. We don't even get sterile gowns unless we order them."

Alison asks that the floor special-order sterile sheets—an order which she will later confirm in writing—and says that she is going to check with the child's pediatrician for the complete sterile policy to follow.

As Alison turns on her heels and begins to exit, Sue Donato picks up two discarded children's lunch trays. As she balances one tray in each hand, two empty plastic cups tip and tumble onto the floor.

"Knew I was going to do that," she says, stymied with her two trays.

Retracing her steps, Alison makes a point of stooping down, picking up the disposable cups, then walking over to plunk them down on the two-tiered disposal cart.

"Thaaaank you," says Sue Donato, a little affectedly.

Back in the baby's room, Alison asks Robin Snell if they could get hold of a sterile sheet to spread out on the floor.

Robin Snell wrinkles her nose and seems to agree. "I can't see the point of wearing a gown and mask and having him play on the floor." Obligingly, the nurse finds one somewhere, and they both unfold and spread out the sheet.

The baby's pediatrician walks in, with Sue Donato marching officiously and silently at his elbow. No, it won't be necessary to wear caps. The severity of the baby's burns doesn't warrant it.

Alison says nothing in reply.

The baby sits on the sterile sheet with two plastic toys, feeding himself his bottle with his one good arm.

Sue Donato peers at him down on the floor and says nothing about the sterile sheet.

The next day, when Alison again makes rounds to check on The Burn Baby, Sue Donato stops her again. She obliquely questions Alison's order for a urinalysis on the small child: Not yet toilet-trained, he will require a sandwich-sized plastic bag taped to his penis.

As she carefully rips off labels from a master sheet and places them in a glass jar, Sue Donato remarks, "If you want to bag him for urine, he'll need a four-point tie, otherwise he'll pull off the bag. Pretty soon after twenty-four hours, you'll have a bleeding bottom." She doesn't stop working as she talks, glancing hard from time to time at Alison.

Not countering the nurse, Alison thinks for a moment. The urinalysis was just a missed part of a routine admission physical.

If she insists that her order be followed, the baby might be endangered, fighting the restraints, rubbing his sores even more raw, if that is possible. She scraps the order. If the baby spikes a temperature later, she'll reconsider.

# 26
# Working with Nurses

"A nurse can make you or break you, particularly as a woman surgeon. They can make or break a case," says a woman surgeon in her late thirties described aptly by a former colleague as tall, determined, and tough, relaxing at home with her husband on a rare free evening. In 1973, she was the first woman to complete a five-year surgical residency and an additional two-year residency in cardiovascular surgery at a mammoth, eminent New York medical center, and she now practices in southern California.

"A scrub nurse," she says, "can hand you the wrong instruments. She can be slower than she ought. Sure, she does it on purpose. Or else, it can be, 'What can we do for you? Can we do this? Do you want this instrument or do you want the one you asked for?' In cardiovascular surgery, many times the nurses have scrubbed on more cases than the residents.

"We had two lady surgeons who came along after I started. But these two girls rubbed the nurses the wrong way and the nurses did everything they could to make them look bad. With a fellow, if they don't like him, they'll do a job, but not a spectacular job. If they *do* like him, then it will be *fantastic.*

"But with girls it's either all for you or all against you, and the majority of nurses are ready not to like you. If you're going to dump on them, if you're not going to give them respect, if you're going to sashay in there and say 'Well, I'm the doctor and *you're* the nurse and you'd better do as *I* say,' forget it. You've had it. And this is the way the two girls I mentioned approached the nurses. These girls aren't there anymore. But for some reason, maybe because I was a nursing student for years and I know how they feel on that side of the fence, it seemed to work out very nicely for me.

"One of those girls was said to have left in the middle of her training to pursue a romance in another city, where she was accepted into a second surgical training program. It was the wrong step to take when your superiors worry you may marry and never use your training anyway. She could never have come back."

The California surgeon neglected to say that the woman who changed programs in the middle of her training is unusually attractive and highly intelligent, all in one striking package. The younger woman surgeon is now steeped in her work as a medical scientist in a southern research facility supported by U.S. government funds. Her silky blonde hair is gracefully swept back in a chignon. Over the slim, firm body of a ballet dancer, she wears a form-fitting black top, a beige wraparound skirt, and platform wedges.

"I've always gotten along with the nurses," says the elegant physician-surgeon, speaking with the slight self-consciousness of someone who knows her beauty and its effect.

"Frequently nurses don't like women doctors because they don't know how to give them orders. I always try to make them feel very important—which I think they *are*. They are an important part of the total job of making the patient feel better. But you have to know how to assert your authority, but not by making the people under you feel lesser. Many of the nurses are extremely devoted. You win them over by making it known you want things to go well for the patient." Another woman doctor, once her resident, has described her as an emasculating female in action, not as smooth as her self-serving answers would indicate. Admitting mistakes is abhorrent to her, as it is to many doctors.

"If you give the impression you are inferior and uneasy, the other person can feel it. It's very important in medicine to take charge. I gave orders to the nurses and I gave them easily."

She is very uncomfortable with the idea that professional women may have special problems related to their sex. "Being female need not be a handicap. You have to have a great deal of confidence. Differences shouldn't be emphasized. After the problems have been aired, described, and understood, there should be a downplaying of male-female dichotomy. Relax and show your work. There's no reason you can't do anything you want to do.''

Uneasy about discussing the reasons for switching programs, she goes on. ''I only applied to the best programs,'' she explains. ''If I didn't get in there, it wasn't worth my time. In New York, I was the second female ever accepted into that surgical program. The first was a very unfeminine woman a few years ahead of me.

''I was *never* interested in nursing. I don't have the personality of the nurse, who has to be a little bit more easily dominated. To be a good nurse one has to take orders and be cooperative and not always take the initiative.

''I'm an only child with all that means in attention. My father thought anything I wanted to do was wonderful. Mother was very pleased with everything I did.''

She flashes a beautiful smile that says she is just a spoiled child.

Thirty years ago, personality types aside, the role expected and accepted of women in medicine was that of nurse. ''I always sensed surprise on the part of the patients when they found out that I was the doctor and not the nurse,'' says a woman surgeon who trained a generation ago in a Catholic hospital. ''But I think that because of the nuns they were used to a female presence that was something other than servile. You knew who ran the place. You *had* to wear a stethoscope in those days because at that time nurses didn't wear stethoscopes. Now they do.''

As a child Alison sensed very early the special awe and respect her parents felt for the physicians practicing in her hometown. On a special level were the town's dozen or so local doctors, who were all the old-fashioned G.P.'s, the kind who worked themselves to the bone and although they may have been forty, usually looked ninety. The local population also included a couple of chiropractors, a doctor of osteopathy, and the town's sole podiatrist, but none of them were held in quite the same esteem by the townsfolk, or her parents, as the M.D.'s. College-educated registered nurses never fell into this elitist, professional category. The physicians were members of the Rotary Club or Lions Club or Elks, male groups composed of a coterie of shopkeepers and professionals in a Pennsylvania milltown where most of the population was blue-collar.

One thing Alison remembers is that her parents talked shop at home, discussing over the dinner table about what was going on at the pharmacy. Both she and her sister knew that later on they would find a niche in one of the medical professions because their parents' chatter always made medicine sound interesting and important.

She can remember her father getting calls at two or three in the morning, having to go in and fill a prescription for someone whose kid was sick. Sometimes Alison would phone and intercept him at a party. It might only have been a call for an over-the-counter bottle of common aspirin. But he would leave the festivities and open the pharmacy for whatever it was. And that just doesn't happen anymore. Finally, he got to the point where he closed down the store on Sundays. But her father's idea of a vacation was sitting in the backyard, not going anywhere, propping up his feet, and not doing anything for a long, long while.

As soon as she was old enough, Alison was eager to help out in the drugstore after school, punching the cash register, straining up to crank the gleaming gearshift soda water spigots. She started at the cash register first, and she can't remember at exactly what age. But her father bought her a stool so she could reach all the keys.

Alison's sister, Helen, two years older than she, decided to become a nurse. The difference in the choice of profession, Alison feels, is one of personality. Academically, her sister would have done well in medical school because she always worked hard and had formed disciplined study habits. Helen still works full-time at a California hospital, although she is married now with two small children. But Helen feels more comfortable with someone telling her what to do, following orders rather than giving them.

At least with women's liberation, women now have an easier time in the choice of profession, Alison feels. And there is nothing more liberating for women than making money. Earning less but with more free time, Helen has the option of spending more time with her family. Marriage Alison feels she can handle, but she is uncertain whether she can efficiently commit herself to both small children and the surgical field. There are three things she likes: medicine, travel, and Mike. There is no way, she says, she can effectively partake adequately of all three and still be an adequate mother.

Both Mike and Alison are unsure whether they want children, ever; in any case Alison would never consider starting a family during her training. The choice is available now that women can control their pregnancies. With a laugh, Alison scoffs at the idea of having children just to insure protection in old age.

A nurse is the bulwark and mainstay of a resident's first year in training. Many times a nurse knows more about medical procedures and medication doses than the resident and can ease problems which loom in patient care.

"At the beginning of the year you ask the nurses an awful lot of questions," says Alison, who seems to have a good relationship with the nurses on a sound, professional basis. "They get very accustomed to telling you what to do. But you still keep up that pretense that *you* are giving the order." An exchange may sound something like this.

"Dr. Merrill?"

"Yes."

"Mr. Smith. I was hanging blood on him and now he has hives. And he has a temperature of 101°."

"Oh, yeah? Oh yeah, is that right? Well, what do you think, Miss Jones?"

"Well, I don't know, doctor. But do you think we ought to disconnect the blood bag and draw blood for a re-cross-matching and maybe send down a urine sample for his transfusion reaction?"

The nurse is delicately intimating that the patient is having an allergic transfusion reaction.

"Yeah! That's a good idea! Why don't we do that."

"How much Benadryl would you like to give?"

"Ah, ma ma ma. Well, uh, uh."

"Would you like to give fifty, Dr. Merrill?"

"Yeah. Yes. Let's give fifty [milligrams]!"

"If I'm in a setting," Alison comments, "where I've got a patient who is having spastic heart problems and arrhythmias and I *know* that I'm supposed to give him lidocaine, I don't always know the appropriate dose. But a lot of times the girls in the Intensive Care Unit do and they'll suggest it. A neurological nurse or a cardiovascular nurse who has been working on the same floor, in the same service, for years and years most of the time knows more than the intern about her subspecialty.

"I feel I get along pretty well with the nurses and I don't particularly object to saying to somebody, 'I don't know.' There's a lot of people who get very hung up about saying 'I don't know,' feeling that it is a show of ignorance and a loss of face. I never quite got into that bind.

"On the other hand, if someone says to me, 'Dr. Merrill, this patient is having P.V.C.'s [premature ventricular contractions],' and I look at the EKG strip and it's a similar graphic rhythm but not P.V.C.'s, I'll say, 'I don't think so, I think it's this.' Or I'll suggest checking it out with somebody else.

"As time goes on, you have a lot more confidence than you had in the beginning of the year and you like to think you know more than they do. You don't want the nurses to tell you what to do anymore. You want to tell *them* what to do. They've been telling you what to do all year long, they're not about to take orders from you. They still assume that you're the same dumb intern that they trained six months ago. Fortunately, the situation is made a lot easier by rotating to another hospital with a new staff.

"Some physicians get trapped into feeling they need to assert their authority. There are doctors who say to that same nice nurse who has been giving them all this key, crucial, helpful advice all year long, 'No, it's *not*,' The implication is, 'You *dummy*. Now I really do know more than you do by this time.' I don't think that's really fair.

"There are physicians who believe that at times you should put nurses *down*. I don't quite buy the rules of the game. I think the time will roll around when I might need them again, and they'd better not tell me, 'You *dummy*. That's not the right dose.'

"I don't like putdownmanship from anybody, but I tell you, if someone put me down, I'd be waiting and looking awfully hard for their next mistake."

# 27
# Hospital Politics

In the cheerfully painted staff lounge used by surgeons between cases, Alison, Dr. Laramy, and Dr. Hans Ness relax with cigarettes and a steady hum of house banter, exchanging experiences. Dr. Laramy recalls his army service as a surgical resident in Korea at Seoul's military hospital, and the sometime absurdities of life with Uncle Sam.

"There were all sorts of nurses in the army who outranked me," Dr. Laramy reminisces on the checkered couch. "They had come in during World War II and found a home and stayed on. The booze was cheap and plentiful and the pay good, and by 1960 some were lieutenant colonels. I was a captain, but I never let them talk down to me. In the beginning they really tried to make me feel they outranked me and would always call me captain. I'd say, 'Yes, nurse?' I made a point of calling them nurse. In the O.R. I told them, 'I'm the surgeon and you're the nurse.' I told them, 'Look, there are plenty of captains in the army, but I'm your only surgeon here. I'm being paid to be the surgeon.' It stopped after a few days. There's no way that I'm going to let a nurse give an order to a doctor."

Dr. Ness smiles, amused. He is a well-liked younger attending surgeon who is trying to build up a private practice for himself, helped by good technical expertise, social charm, an unbounded enthusiasm for surgery, an even disposition, and a quick wit.

Turning his swivel chair toward Alison, he asks her devilishly, "Do you detect a little male chauvinism there?"

Alison glances at Dr. Laramy's expression. He is staring at Dr. Ness open-mouthed. To Dr. Laramy it is not a question of male or female differences, but the business of asserting hierarchical authority between doctor and nurse. He is flabbergasted someone might consider his attitude chauvinist.

As part of their scuttlebutt, they discuss a previous woman surgical resident who left a bad memory. After surgery, she once told a private patient that she had been allowed to do his entire case. The patient said nothing at the time but later refused to pay the private attending's bill. After all, he had hired a particular surgeon in all good faith to perform his surgery.

Yearning for a hurried, bracing cup of coffee and a snack, Alison heads down the stairs toward the basement cafeteria. Eventually she steps into a large room, bright with recessed fluorescent lighting, white walls alternating with yellow, sparkling white floors, white and chrome tables, and blonde wood chairs upholstered in garish colors.

Passing the metal-and-glass cafeteria case topped with an arrangement of anemic wax flowers, and the grill with its menu of hot and cold sandwiches, she stops next to a series of beverage machines and presses the button for coffee. Next she selects a prepackaged chocolate sundae, and then looks out over the room.

A group of slightly rumpled residents, hair tousled, white jackets over wrinkled green scrub suits, slouch over their table as they talk. An array of ballpoint pens, mimeographed sheets, and stethoscopes jam the pockets of their whites, which hang down in front from the weight.

A medical student wanders in looking for a friendly face, holding a tray uncertainly.

Nurses come in and out, some with coats and handbags.

Someone's bleeper sounds off amidst the background chatter. One of the residents pushes back his chair, which screeches against the floor, and hurries to call from one of the beige wall phones strategically placed along white pillars around the room.

Alison is surprised to see Jerry Kohler, her chief resident, sitting at a table in the front of the room. Jerry rarely comes to the cafeteria, bringing a sandwich every day, neatly and carefully prepared by his wife, who often adds an extra tidbit like carrot sticks.

He is alone, and since his presence is so obvious in the room, she decides to join him. Jerry has just helped one of his residents evaluate a new surgical admission who arrived in the Emergency Room.

Tonight he seems to be in a talkative mood, and he thumps his fist on the cafeteria table to emphasize the strength of his feelings. "The whole subject of women in medicine pisses me off. I give my wife a paycheck and if it's not enough, tough. But she's got that, and in return I expect her to keep the house in order. I do expect to find the house neat and tidy when I come home. That's her *job*."

Later Alison will comment that "Kohler offends you so rapidly you don't even want to hear what he has to say."

For the moment Alison wisely says little, looking at Kohler with a half smile. He is not actually looking at her as he talks, but gazes distantly. Alison sees a tall, broad-shouldered, heavy-set man of about thirty-two, square-jawed and big-boned. Outspoken, he worries little about the effect of his remarks on others. His position as chief resident assures a modicum of respect from the younger residents under his supervision and subject to his criticism. As every interesting case comes up that the junior assistant residents anticipate with relish, Jeremy Kohler will appear in the operating room and tend to hog the surgery, keeping the interesting work to himself and letting his residents handle the post-op care of the patient. Perhaps he feels he's getting his own back for those years as a more junior resident when, as he once said, "I was shit upon. I was shit upon."

"I have an aunt who is much older than I am," Kohler continues now, still without looking directly at Alison, but across the room. "Fifteen years older. I wouldn't want her to hear that. But, anyway, she's a pediatrician. One of her children is going to be a candidate for a psychiatrist someday. The other one is going to turn out to be Patricia Hearst. She's had a housekeeper to bring up her children. Now who has to be there to *train* the housekeeper? The mother has got to be there to supervise.

"Who is that unfair to?" he asks rhetorically. "The *children*."

"Kohler will frequently carp about women in medicine," says Alison later of the chief resident. "He tries to defend himself about not being all that prejudiced because he has an aunt who is a pediatrician. But he also makes scandalous comments about her."

Muttering to Kohler, Alison mentions that some women may have decided not to have children.

Kohler spreads his arms wide. "Great! Tie their tubes as soon as they graduate and you've solved the whole problem."

Alison still continues to smile. She'd never be able to convince someone like that. His mind is already made up and it's just too late in the game.

Alison will sometimes talk about Sally Damian, a tall, lanky, plain, serious-minded surgical resident a year ahead of her. With Alison, Sally is one of the three women in a surgical training program consisting of thirty residents. Unfortunately, she can be offensively outspoken when angry, and she sometimes has had problems with Kohler. She found that he frequently assigned her to Dr. Cecil Towers, a favorite among the medical students. He is a private surgeon who clamps every minute capillary, carefully exposes every thin, elusive fascial tissue plain. For a thyroidectomy, it is said he once took twenty minutes to decide where to best place the incision for the least noticeable scar to the patient. If a medical student asks him how he opens the skin, he launches into a fifteen-minute discourse on his procedure and surgical philosophy. He is a fascinating surgeon to watch wielding a scalpel, and he has the fewest post-op complications of any surgeon in the hospital. However, he eats up more hours than any other surgeon to complete one case, which meant that Sally Damian was scrubbing on relatively fewer cases. Sally felt she was getting less experience than the male residents, and seethed over her predicament.

One night Sally sought Alison out in the comfortable, double-bunk room reserved for the on-call residents, to ask advice about her problem with Jerry Kohler. Unlike City Hospital, where the residents had to filch sheets and blankets from the floor's linen closet, here the room is always tidied and the beds promptly made in the morning by the hospital's housekeeping staff.

Alison warned Sally to be more tactful in her complaints. "You shouldn't let it go if something like that happens and it bothers you," Alison told Sally. "But you should handle the problem carefully. If you give him a rational argument, you'll have a better chance. Tell Kohler that everybody ought to have a chance to scrub with Dr. Towers."

Unfortunately, Sally didn't have the right lid on her anger, and stormed up to Kohler and demanded a change in her O.R. assignments. Sally didn't like Kohler to begin with, and he knew it. She didn't take enough pains to mask her anger and dislike. So Kohler said O.K. and assigned her to the cases of a surgeon who rarely gave anything away at her level of training. She went from doing something in the operating room to doing nothing.

If Sally does not get her way, she will only reluctantly fulfill her hospital responsibilities. Many of the residents will behave that way, following an unwritten hospital rule: If you don't help me or teach me, I won't do your scutwork. But Alison claims that Sally's behavior may be more noticeable because she is a woman.

However, Sally Damian talks little now and has an aura about her which seems slightly removed.

"Traditionally," says Alison, "appendectomies and hemorrhoidectomies are done by surgical interns. But you still depend on the good graces of your superiors. You really can't say; 'Is it my turn? Is it my turn?' A lot is unsaid. We could just as easily steal the skin stitches from the medical students."

Alison actually likes scrubbing with Towers. He is slow, but then she isn't the fastest surgeon either, and he gives a beautiful demonstration in anatomy as he goes along. He cares enough about his patients to worry about the tiniest detail of their care.

The other woman in the university's surgical program, whom Alison will occasionally mention, is Dorothea Richards, a vivacious, outspoken resident. Dorothea Richards is a legend among residents, who complain frequently about the lack of sleep. On the weekends, Dorothea goes scuba diving in the Bahamas. Scorning a car, she pedals a ten-speed bicycle or takes a motorcycle to the hospital, if possible, and rides her own horse for recreation. She also water-skis and lifts weights. According to one well-known story, she once brought her horse, lame, to Lakeside Hospital, tethered him someplace, and in between doing surgery or seeing a patient would rush out to soak his infected foot.

Alison is both admiring and incredulous over Dorothea's unlimited zip. "When I come home, I pretty much collapse and Mike takes over. I can't imagine coming home and riding a horse!"

Sometimes Alison jokes that Dorothea Richards might be hyperthyroid, suffering from an overactive thyroid with its corollary manifestation of excessive energy

Perhaps with intuition as to how some women adjust to a very competitive marketplace where they are represented in small numbers, Mike has another explanation. "Dorothea Richards is trying to be better than any man, a superwoman," he says.

# 28
# Emergency Room:
# Crises and Gobble-Gobbles

Up on the surgical floor, Alison Merrill's bleeper sounds insistently, like a pesky mosquito buzzing in her ear. The message is simply, "Call 2626." But Alison immediately recognizes the Emergency Room's number. At the nearest phone, she dials the number.

The E.R. nurse tells her that Dr. Emory Busch, an attending, has a female patient in the Emergency Room. The staff physician on duty in the E.R. has taken a first look and diagnosed peritonitis, and now the woman is waiting to be examined by the surgical resident.

In one of the E.R. treatment rooms, a tiny place just about wide enough for a bed on one side and cabinets of pharmaceuticals and a stainless-steel sink on the other, Alison begins to question a tall, blonde, mature-looking fifteen-year-old named Flora Sims. The gaunt, stricken girl is lying uncomfortably on the bed with her knees bent tensely up to her chest.

"When did the pains start?"

"Last night about 7:30. They woke me up."

"What are they like?"

"Like the worst pains I've ever had. Like pains running through me."

"Do they come and go?"

"Yes."

"Did you vomit?"

"Yes."

"How many times?"

"Over and over."

"Did you eat anything?"

"No." She looks to the side of the bed.

"Did they do any bloodwork?"

"No, they just took X-rays."

Outside the room, Dr. Busch is talking to the mother, a serene-looking woman who is calmly concerned about her daughter.

"Is she allergic to penicillin?"

"No," replies the mother proudly. "She's never been sick. As far as I know, she's never had penicillin."

Dr. Busch puts an arm around the mother and congratulates her. "That's rare nowadays."

"I don't believe in taking a child to the doctor just for a cold," says the mother crisply.

Walking into the treatment room, Dr. Busch begins his own line of questioning.

"When was your last menstrual period?"

"It just started."

"Is there any chance you could be pregnant?"

"No." Her answers are quick and definite.

"Have you ever had inflammation of the tubes or anything like that?"

"No, I've never felt this sick before. I got sick while I was out with my boyfriend, and he had to take me home. I started to shake and I got really white."

"Any fever?"

"No real fever. Just shaking."

"Didn't pass out, though?"

"No." She shakes her head. Her voice is tight with pain.

Turning to the nurse, who has been standing silently for instructions while leaning against the sink, Dr. Busch asks, "Do you have time to put an N-G tube down her?"

"Yes," says the nurse briskly. A nursing-school pin is stuck into the wing of her starched cap. She hurries out the door to execute the order.

Dr. Busch and Alison will ask for more lab tests. Alison will examine the girl's X-rays in a joint effort to unravel the cause of her intense abdominal pain.

As the two physicians turn to leave without more ado, Dr. Busch asks Alison, "How is that little Burn Baby? Is he all right?"

"Yes," says Alison. "Some escars [scabs] are beginning to form and he took his first whirlpool bath yesterday."

She walks into the center of the well-equipped Emergency Room, the hub of a wheel where all Lakeside's medical problems are duly sorted, pigeonholed, and referred to the appropriate service. It occupies one large wing of the ground floor, with its own ambulance alley, a special parking lot, and a pedestrian entrance separate from the hospital's main entrance around the corner. The Emergency Room is actually a complex of rooms, some with a specialized purpose. One treatment room holds special equipment for combating cardiac arrest with instant efficiency; another room is the suture room, with all the necessary equipment to repair lacerations. An Olympic Papoose Board dangles from the wall, with canvas flaps and laces to immobilize a child during stitching. The Papoose Board is a juvenile strait jacket.

The complex includes a small blood and urine lab as well as an X-ray room, both opening into a main circular hall which follows the curve of the rounded Emergency Room. In the main room in the center, two doctors and three nurses sit near shelves and rooms containing I.V. stands and solutions, plastic tubing, Levine tubes, suction machines, defibrillator paddles, EKG's, tracheotomy sets, sterile suture sets, every kind of bandage pad, bottles of Betadine solution, hydrogen peroxide, benzoin tincture, and boxes of Steri-Strip skin closures.

"This is a well-run hospital. I'd even be a patient here," says Alison, paying Lakeside the ultimate compliment from a doctor.

Shortly, the E.R. is busily handling a twelve-year-old boy who slashed his hand working on his bicycle, a four-year-old boy who cut his foot on a dock, a man who sliced his left finger on a metal partition at work, and a woman with vulvar lacerations whose husband assaulted her vaginally with a candle.

A small boy is rolled in on a stretcher, his mouth swollen and bleeding. He is missing all his front teeth, which he clutches protectively in one hand.

"What happened to you, sonny?" asks one of the E.R. staff physicians, a man whose face looks pale and tired.

"I bumped." His mouth is swollen, his lips have a hard time meeting to form words.

"We'll keep your teeth, sonny. Do you keep them under your pillow for the fairy?"

No answer. The lips quiver slightly. It is such an effort to speak.

In another treatment room, a fat thirty-four-year-old woman is slumped over on her side on the bed. She is practically motionless, having overdosed earlier in the day on tranquilizers. A doctor walks in to take her blood pressure. He picks up an arm which is limp and flaccid and she looks at him through half-closed eyes, her mouth slightly open and drooling. Her blood pressure will be monitored at regular intervals, and she will be observed continuously. Before she can be released some twenty-four to thirty-six hours later, a psych resident will have to certify that the women is not on the verge of committing suicide.

The four-year-old child yells in the background.

"Have we admitted that nosebleed yet?" asks the tired-looking physician.

"Yeah," answers one of the nurses.

He laughs. "How long has he been here?"

"Oh, only since 7:00 this morning."

"Oh, well." He shrugs. "We treated him along the way."

The woman who O.D.'d gets up sluggishly from the bed and starts to stumble toward the treatment room's wooden door with its small viewing window. She motions through the window. Since the door is closed, her babble is unintelligible. The sallow physician turns to look at her, and then goes back to his conversation with one of the nurses.

"Oh, she just wants someone to talk to," he says. "She's psychotic. Psych is deciding whether or not to admit her."

The woman hesitantly opens the door, stumbles a few steps through the doorway in her short white hospital gown, and makes a few guttural sounds. She wants to go to the bathroom. A nurse brings a bedpan.

In the center, an oversized desk dominates the room. A cardboard box of stale doughnuts lies next to a recent issue of *The New Physician*. The dial of a radio is set to dreamy music. A fire-engine-red phone sits glaringly atop a G.E. radio dispatcher.

Outside, in the Emergency Room waiting area, a barefoot middle-aged lady with frazzled hair is pacing the floor in her dark-green short nylon nightie, a white hospital gown thrown askew over her shoulders, a cigarette dangling from her fingertips. She walks nervously to and fro, like a wild beast pacing a cage.

At the desk, a fresh-faced nurse in an immaculate white pantsuit uniform is calling the state police.

"It's a confusing story," she opens, after identifying herself as Lucy Walters from Lakeside's Emergency Room. Her phone call has a chummy tone and the sound of repeated routine. The police receive many calls from Lakeside's Emergency Room. Like Boy Scouts, they are often called in to do favors for the E.R. staff.

"Their phone is out of order, and we can't reach this woman's family. Can you go by and tell them to pick up their mother?"

Yes, the police agree to help right away.

Long auburn hair streaming loosely down her neck, the nurse sits back in the swivel desk chair and groans. She talks about the lady in the green nightie. "The family dropped her off just like that. In her bedclothes with no shoes. There's nothing really wrong with the woman except that she's a bit tipsy, and she is not going to be admitted. The E.R. staff gave her $5 to get home. She took a ride all around town. Finally the driver gave up, put his flag down, and brought her back here.

"This happens often at holiday time. People will come in here and dump their cantankerous parent who is getting in their way. Or they want to go away for the holidays and don't want their old mother. Then the hospital can't find the family. Social Service will have to get in on it like a detective agency and locate the family. The E.R. has a name for them. We call them the gobble-gobbles or the turkeys. These are the fakes.

"We have a list of drug addicts who come in here regularly asking for Demerol for some trumped-up complaint or other.

"One woman came in here asking for a new pair of shoes.

"At 5:30 A.M. yesterday I picked up a call from a girl and her boyfriend. They had just had intercourse and hadn't taken anything and thought that the wrath of God might be on them. Was there any pill or shot we could give her to prevent her from getting pregnant?

"Another type is the mother who brings her child at 3:00 in the morning into the Emergency Room when the child has been sick for a week. She tells the child, 'See what a good mother I am to bring you in here at this hour?'

"Or else you hear, 'He's been lying down on the couch for four days without moving, and we finally decided to turn him over.' That's exactly what one family said."

Suddenly, Alison is called urgently into the cardiac arrest treatment room. A white-haired comatose woman is lying on the stretcher. One doctor wrestles with a laryngoscope to begin intubating the woman, establishing a tubed path past the layrnx into the trachea to rush oxygen into her lungs.

"This should be a dental admission," he complains as he struggles to establish a patent, or unobstructed, airway.

On a shelf under the stretcher is a helter-skelter pile of clothes—underwear, skirt, sweater—all carelessly heaped.

The woman regurgitates, and they quickly suction her mouth.

One breast is very obviously missing, and there is an ugly scar on the chest wall from the radical mastectomy.

Through her stethoscope, Alison is listening to the woman's chest. "I don't hear her on this side."

Now Alison is going to put in a subclavian I.V., an intravenous catheter inserted into an important vein situated under the clavicle.

By this time, about sixteen people are crowded around the stretcher.

A policeman saunters up to the periphery of the group and stares around the room self-consciously, a pistol at the ready on his hip. A string of bullets gleam in a circle in his cartridge belt. "Where is the woman who O.D.'d?" he asks. He has brought the vials snatched from the woman's home and medicine cabinet.

A nurse takes the pill containers: folic acid, Premarin, Darvon, Seconal, and Valium. The bottles of folic acid, a vitamin preparation for anemia, and Premarin, an estrogen compound, are nearly full. The empty ones tell the story. She has swallowed a cocktail of Darvon, Seconal, and Valium. It is a very deliberate suicide attempt.

Eventually, the woman on the stretcher resumes breathing and the intravenous line is in place.

"For someone who stopped breathing, she looks pretty good," Alison comments as she walks back into the E.R.'s main section.

The E.R. physician ambles up to her, his hands resting inside his long white coat pockets. "We had an interesting case last night. Fresh-water drowning. Hemoglobinuria and lactic acidosis. His urine was like red wine."

Of course Alison understands what he means. In shock and without oxygen, the Interesting Case's red blood cells burst open and released hemoglobin, which was excreted in the urine, while large amounts of lactic acid accumulated in the tissues. It's just a normal snatch of E.R. banter.

When Flora Sims looks up and sees Alison walking into the examining room, she manages to joke a little. "I'm still alive. Haven't died yet."

"When was the last time you had anything to eat?" The nurse who inserted the N-G tube has just told Alison that the girl disgorged a full stomach of food.

"Yesterday at lunch."

"But you've had some aspirin, so you've taken water." Often patients will not consider water and medication as food. But if there is a chance the girl will undergo surgery in the abdominal region, it is important that her stomach be empty to avoid her vomiting under the effects of anesthesia.

"Oh, yeah. My mother gave them to me all through the night."

"Did it do anything?"

Flora Sims shakes her head. "No."

Alison mentally catalogues her symptoms. She has an alarmingly high white blood count, 22,700. When Alison softly felt and tapped her abdomen on both sides, the girl's pain was much more intense when Alison lifted the slight pressure of her hands—an indication of severe bilateral rebound pain. Flora Sims also has a hard abdomen, stiff with pain; and no sounds from the intestine, which indicates that peristalsis has stopped, an involuntary reaction to pain. These symptoms point to the possibility of a ruptured appendix.

Paging Dr. Busch in another part of the hospital, she tells him it could be a perforated appendix. She mentions the omnipresent suspicion of P.I.D., pelvic inflammatory disease, associated with gonorrhea. They decide to observe the patient for a little while longer.

Flora Sims will be sent up to the pediatric floor. There are no more beds in the Adolescent Unit.

# 29
# Pulling the Curtain

An old, old woman with a shockingly emaciated physical appearance lies on her side in another E.R. examining room. Her eyes are staring and motionless. She is tranquilized, sedated, or doped on Valium. The orthopedic resident has his foot stretched up to her armpit for counter-traction, pulling her arm in an attempt to snap the arm's ball joint back into its socket. A nursing home inmate, she has a three-week-old dislocation of the shoulder but has just been carried into the hospital.

Eva Belman, a third-year medical student, goes to take a look. "It's great for anatomy," she says. Watching the orthopedic resident through the doorway to the examining room, Alison nods disgustedly. "You see the poor care people get in nursing homes and it sours you on them. They're holding patterns for the old until they die."

Finally, a slightly drunken middle-aged man in a trench coat arrives to pick up his slightly drunken wife in the green nightie. The couple stares silently, sullenly, and hostilely at each other like two wary boxers paired off in the ring. The woman doesn't seem in any hurry to leave the hospital. He will have trouble moving her physically.

Next, Thomas Fargis, a patient eligible for Medicaid, is being admitted for treatment of a carcinoma on the floor of his mouth. Alison is called in to see him. Residents always cover the service cases.

She checks and stares at a gross white mass which crosses the midline of his tongue. "How long have you had this?" Alison asks the tall wiry man, not too far from skid row, with a thick hillbilly accent.

"Darned if I know."

No, he doesn't smoke much.

No, he doesn't drink much. Maybe three or four beers a day. He is shaking slightly. His responses seem muffled and slow. Alison recognizes some of the symptoms of chronic alcoholism and is listening to his answers with a grain of salt.

"Hasn't your mouth bothered you?"

"Not particularly."

A paternal and concerned couple step into the room. She is short and fat; he is tall, slightly potbellied. "Hello," they say, "we keep him for Social Service."

The woman explains the background of Thomas Fargis' presence in Lakeside's Emergency Room. "Thursday night I saw he was having trouble eating. He never complained of any pain at all. He'd sit and run his thumb over his cheek and I'd say, 'Do you have any pain?' and he'd say no. He began to use mouthwash several times a day."

"What I want to know is, is he basically dry?"

"Yes." The couple rushes into the answer, speaking together like a Greek chorus. The woman's head bobs up and down.

"He's disabled," says the woman. "He has disability for T.B. He has some brain damage from alcoholism."

After examining the man's mouth carefully, Alison puzzles over the resectability of the tumor, whether the surgical removal of the growth will actually cure the patient without too much destruction; whether in its present size an operation would require radical removal of part of his jaw and a node dissection, an exploration for a spread of total disease to the lymph nodes in the neck. She thinks the tumor should be treated first with X-rays to reduce its size. By phone, she reaches Jerry Kohler, who mentions he doesn't want the man admitted to the surgical floor unless the ugly mass is resectable.

Then she puts a call through to Dr. Perry Webster, the head of the surgical department at Lakeside. "Is Dr. Webster still in the house?" she asks his secretary. When Dr. Webster comes to the phone, Alison outlines her reservations. Yes, he will come down to the Emergency Room.

5:10 P.M., and waiting in the E.R.

Dr. Webster arrives in a business suit and takes charge. Examining Thomas Fargis, who is blissfully unconcerned with the conversation swimming around him, Dr. Webster takes the opportunity to question Eva Belman, who is watching and listening.

"When you see this in the oral cavity, what do you look for?"

"Smoking and drinking."

"When you have these conditions, a lesion in the mouth, what other lesions do you worry about?"

"Lesions in the larynx and lungs."

Dr. Webster turns toward the guardian couple. "He has some irreversible damage. It's malignant."

"Go ahead and admit him," he recommends to Alison, "and start some studies on him."

The patient just listens indifferently, sitting up on the bed, leaning against the wall with his hands behind his head.

"If you check the neck"—Dr. Webster fingers the glands on both sides of the neck—"I think it is a grade 1."

Dr. Webster is saying that Fargis has the earliest kind of cancer, grade 1, the lowest number in a scale denoting malignant aggressiveness and the involvement of the other tissues.

Dr. Webster does not feel any hard cancerous lymph nodes in the neck.

"We had to fight to get him to clean his plate," says the woman. "He said he never took out his dentures for nobody."

"He has carcinoma, cancer," Dr. Webster tells her.

"I saw him washing his mouth several times a day," the woman repeats. "A doctor examined him in January for Social Service. He went so fast, it's possible he didn't see it."

Dr. Webster leaves for the day. The man says he is a diabetic and hasn't had any lunch. Alison recommends he had better grab a snack in the hospital cafeteria.

Although she hasn't asked him to come down, Jerry Kohler arrives to take a look at Fargis in the Emergency Room. He puts on a rubber glove.

"This disease is extremely rare in persons with good personal hygiene," says Kohler as he roughly passes his fingers over the insides of the patient's mouth, pulling the skin in all directions.

For once, the man has reacted to pain. He grunts, shakes his head as if to throw off the hurt.

Standing behind Thomas Fargis, Kohler feels the lymph nodes in his neck. With the joy of discovery, he makes a silent face and points to it energetically. "There are several round pebbles in here."

Alison in turn presses her hands into the man's skin. "Very teeny little pebbles."

Kohler is making the point that the cancer has already traveled and spread to the lymph nodes. "It's there, it's hard, it doesn't belong there."

"For the sake of argument, he has had T.B.," Alison replies. Hardened lymph glands could be the result of an assault from T.B. as well as cancer.

They leave Thomas Fargis to be fully processed for admission to the surgical floor.

Moving to the following patient, Alison examines a forty-year-old man who is complaining of a pain in his right testicle.

"Where is the pain?" Alison asks.

"It goes all the way around all the way down to the testicle. It's been going on for a month now." An articulate man, he sits on the edge of a bed in a room closed off by a curtain, with his trousers around his ankles.

Suddenly the loudspeaker attracts Alison's attention and stops her midway into the examination. "M-set, M-set. Room 303."

Alison whirls out of the room without another word. She leaves her poor patient with his trousers down at his feet, not stopping to tell him he can dress for the time being because she will be gone for a considerable time.

Alison is running very fast, past startled visitors ambling down the hospital corridors. "That's a child's room," she blurts out, slightly out of breath. Clop, clop, clop, clop, clop, noisily down the hall. Up the stairs, all three flights, two by two. Alison is huffing and puffing but not losing speed. Behind her a few feet on the stairs, a nurse is also running as fast as she can, also breathing heavily. She is trying to catch up to Alison, but can't. The nurse is toting a small metal box of emergency drugs.

An unusual number of white coats are clip-clopping down the hall and converging on Room 303. Their loud footsteps echo in the hall.

In Room 303, a small three-year-old boy has his pajama top pushed up around his neck. Blue crepe paper is twirled around the metal frame of his bed.

Craig Armstrong, who is also completing a surgical rotation at Lakeside, is pumping the boy's chest, and the child's head is bouncing up and down on the mattress with the violence of the pumping. A nurse has placed a triangular mask on the boy's face and squeezes a black bag to force air into the little body whose lips are already blue.

Alison's face is tense and her voice shaking. "Get me a tourniquet."

A nurse unceremoniously throws a tourniquet across the bed.

If the veins are collapsed, a tourniquet will help locate a usable vein in the foot for a cutdown to start an intravenous line.

Alison then asks for a cutdown tray, a sterile pack of instruments to cut into the vein for the intravenous catheter.

A father saunters over from the waiting area at the end of the hall. "Is someone with my Bobby?" he asks curiously. Another little boy has his leg in traction in the next bed; he is completely ignored.

"Pull the curtain, Dotty, will you?" asks Dr. Ellie York, the pediatric resident, of one of the nurses. The curtain is quickly pulled around the neighboring bed. With luck the child will not be too frightened by the excitement surrounding his roommate.

The grandparents of the stricken boy have gone to sit and wait on the chairs in the hall. They seem to be accepting. The doctors are doing everything they can.

The little boy's pediatric resident is calm. "He wasn't without oxygen for very long. He went into laryngeal spasms. He's a surgery patient and was operated on a few days ago to remove a web in that area. He had a respiratory arrest right before my eyes. We needed to tube him but he was clamping his teeth. There was a bag next to the bed, which was lucky. I started to bag him, but it was insufficient oxygenation through clenched teeth so I called M-set. There was no cardiac arrest."

Nevertheless, the emergency team is giving the child a cardiac massage while attempting to oxygenate him sufficiently.

A very young woman in a yellow T-shirt and blue jeans, carrying a shopping bag full of belongings, is walking nonchalantly down the hall toward the room, gazing at all the people surrounding the doorway. Without asking any questions, she pushes her way through the crowd into the room and looks silently at the child on the bed, with tubes running from his mouth and from his leg; at the tight knot of so many doctors and nurses crowded around him, even jamming the doorway.

She walks out of the room with her head bent over, and suddenly breaks down into loud sobs in the hallway.

It is the mother.

"It's all right, it's all right," says Kirstin Fernie, who is now doing a pediatric rotation at Lakeside.

"Shit," says Kirstin a while later. "That's not too cool to say in any case. I didn't realize that was the mother. She looked so young."

The grandmother rushes over and puts her arm comfortingly around the young woman. They hurry into a conference room and Dr. York follows.

Alison has successfully inserted an intravenous catheter, and life-saving medication is already being pumped into the boy's system. The team has ordered STAT blood gases, a single blood sample which will be analyzed for its oxygen and carbon dioxide levels, bicarbonate content, and pH level. A portable X-ray machine for a STAT X-ray is already being wheeled in.

In a short while, the slim young blue-jeaned mother pushes out the door of the conference room and marches stiffly toward her son's room. Her eyes are dry-eyed and narrowed, her jaw is set in tight determination.

"That's my son," she says in a hostile voice, as if the medical staff were keeping her from him in a time of crisis.

Dr. York hurriedly runs to fill the doorway of the boy's room and bar the way. "If you love him, stay out of there and let us do our job. Right now, you're not the right person in there."

The mother gives up and never reaches her son's bedside. She turns back into the hall and again starts to sob. Again she is led back into the conference room.

A few minutes later, Dr. York comes back, rattled. "I gave her Valium and I thought she was calmed down." The mother had been sedated to make her malleable, but the pills did not work.

"Oof," says an older M.D. in civilian clothes, sighing with relief as he strides out of the room.

The little boy is breathing again.

Alison is amazed as she walks out of the room, directing her steps briskly back toward the Emergency Room. "I really don't know why in a case like that they should expect me to wait for gloves and to wait for spray." For a cutdown to insert an I.V., sterile procedure is usually followed. The surgeon wears sterile gloves for cutting into the vein, and the skin is sprayed with antiseptic Betadine prior to being cut open. The attending physician had come in and yelled at Alison, "Isn't that the worst thing I've ever seen! No gloves. No prep. Close that thing up."

"The attending usually never makes it to arrests," Alison explains. "That's usually handled by the nursing and resident staff. He has no idea how hard it is for you to get equipment or gloves at a time like that. They didn't have any gloves in the room. The pediatric I.C.U. would have had them, but the floor wouldn't."

In the Emergency Room, a resident looks up levelly at Alison from an opened book he is leafing through on the steel desk. It is a black book marked "Poisoning" in shiny yellow letters.

"That was completely unnecessary to shout at you," he says, shaking his head disapprovingly. "It was rude and unnecessary for a thoracic surgeon to tell you to wear gloves. Why didn't he get there before?"

Alison nods in agreement.

"Was that the little boy we readmitted this morning who had a web?" asks a nurse.

Alison says yes.

"He looked pretty bad this morning. He was spitting and vomiting. Did they trach him?" A "trach" is short for a tracheotomy, a surgical opening in the trachea in order to insert a tube to facilitate the passage of air.

"No, it wasn't necessary."

Forty-five minutes later, Alison returns to the bespectacled man who is complaining of pain in his right testicle. He is still waiting patiently in the same examining room.

Alison decides that neither the testes nor the spermatic cord feel tender.

"I don't feel any hernias at all. The cord doesn't feel big or tender," she tells him, and after all that waiting she sends him home.

2:15 A.M. An older black man with grizzling hair twists in pain on the stretcher. His scrotum, the size of a football, is grossly distended from loops of bowel which have fallen down into it.

Dr. Hans Ness, splendidly dressed for this hour of the night in a houndstooth suit and polka dot tie, is with the man when Alison walks into the examining room.

Unable to get an adequate history, Dr. Ness asks to speak to his worried daughter. She tells him that her father has had a hernia for some time but was always successful in pushing the bulge back into his body. This time, the lump wouldn't ease back inside.

Technically, Dr. Ness quietly explains, her father has an "incarcerated inguinal hernia."

Calmly Dr. Ness clarifies the emergency operation. "The bowel is twisted, strangulated. We may have to make an abdominal incision to pull back the bowel. If the bowel is already dead, we'll have to cut it and sew it back together. It will take at least two and a half hours."

Dr. Ness is on the E.R. phone to the operating room's scheduling nurse to reserve a room. "This is the midnight cowboy," he says with a smile.

Alison laughs. Dr. Ness is working hard to build up his practice. Three surgeons are on call to the Emergency Room for patients who arrive with a surgical problem but without the name of a specific surgeon. Sometimes covering the other on-call surgeons, Dr. Ness is in at any hour, hustling patients in the E.R. in the dead of night. Hence, he is affectionately called—and dubs himself—the midnight cowboy. Most of his surgery is done at night.

"Dr. Ness," Alison will say, "is the classic general surgeon. He just loves trauma. He just grooves. He gets up in the middle of the night and trudges in through sleet, snow, or hail."

But Dr. Ness never loses his cool or his sense of humor. During the surgery, when loops of bowel literally pop out of the incisions, he announces, "Oh, oh! Ladies and gentlemen, it's a boy." Laughing and assisting at the same time, Alison moves away from the table long enough to cough.

"Have you seen a doctor?" asks the circulating nurse facetiously.

Alison edges back to the table. "Have you any idea how difficult it is, being a resident, to see a doctor?"

The "circ" nods, smiling sympathetically.

The anesthesiologist and a male scrub nurse discuss a steak dinner.

Meanwhile, the old man's family sacks out on the couches of the darkened lobby. When it is over, Dr. Ness will stop by to give them news of their father.

They finish in the O.R. at 5:50 in the morning.

After early-morning rounds, shortly after 7:00 A.M. and a fitful hour's sleep, Alison runs down the stairs toward the basement cafeteria. Before she gets there, on the first floor, her bleeper goes off once again.

"I should have gone to the bathroom before this call," she mutters as she dials the surgical I.C.U.

"What was her pressure when she did that?" she asks into the phone. "Was it low then? We'd better open up her I.V. a little bit and I'll stop by and see her shortly. How much urine is she putting out?" The nurse gives her the patient's urine output over the last hour, and Alison scribbles "80 cc.s" with her ballpoint pen on the pants of her rumpled green scrub suit.

Dr. Ness comes running up to Alison as she is about to start again in the direction of the cafeteria. "I have a beautiful case! A Beautiful Case!" he cries happily. "A service case. This girl, twenty years old, came into the E.R. two nights ago with vague lower-quadrant pain. Today she came in with severe bilateral abdominal pain with a chandelier sign." The chandelier effect is a common term used when there is so much pain upon examination, the patient seems to jump off the bed reaching for a chandelier. "She has a high white count. They took a chest film. There's free air under the diaphragm.

"It's either," says Dr. Ness, pointing an enthusiastic finger at Alison, "a perforated ulcer in the stomach or duodenum or a perforated portion of the gastrointestinal tract which has released air into the abdomen." These are situations which usually require immediate surgical repair.

Alison watches Dr. Ness disappear quickly down the hall toward a sign, white letters on a red background: "Surgical Suite. No Admittance."

Crossing the lobby, Alison sees the young blue-jeaned mother of the little boy, so very young, come flying across the room to the bank of elevators. Desperately, the girl pushes and pushes the button for an elevator which won't come. She bursts into tears and the sound of her sobs overflows into the lobby.

Her son had a second respiratory arrest at two and a third one at six earlier that morning. A final cardiac arrest followed closely on the heels of the respiratory arrest at six.

A nurse comes out of the elevator and leads the young mother by the arm. Visitors begin to stream into the lobby, and nobody seems to notice the small storm center of pain. Outside, it is the beginning of a beautiful day.

In the staff lounge, Craig Armstrong, still in his scrubs, is drinking coffee. He seems sad, subdued, and puzzled. "The only thing that could have saved him was a bronchoscopy [a tube passed down the trachea into the bronchus].'' But there was no bronchoscope in a small enough pediatric size, a piece of equipment used in more specialized, pediatric hospitals.

Highstrung and emotional as she is, the mother probably feels her absence made a difference in the last moments of her child's life. She will never know.

# 30
# Women on the Table

"How is the pain?" Alison asks Flora Sims as she stops by to see her before surgery.

"Still lots and lots."

Flora Sims lies under a bright yellow bedspread, half propped on pillows, with a nasogastric tube plummeting down her right nostril, down her esophagus and into her stomach.

"Are they going to take this out?" She points to the N-G tube. "I can't stand it." She looks groggy, her eyes half closed. She is drowsy from sedation preliminary to surgery.

"Mom?" She calls to her mother on the other side of the curtain. "Did you get him?"

"Who?"

"Steve."

"No."

Flora Sims says nothing, but looks disappointed.

"Will you operate too?" she asks Alison.

"I assist."

"In spite of all she's said," says Dr. Busch as he begins to trace a midline incision with a scalpel on Flora Sims's anesthetized body in the O.R., "I think we're going to find a P.I.D. But I can't be sure, so that's why we're operating."

By fractions of an inch, he cuts through the skin, fat, a tough membranous tissue called fascia, and muscle. He pulls open the wound delicately with his fingers, forcing the muscle apart. Then he cuts the thin, transparent peritoneum and plunges into the abdomen.

"If the mother had been in the room when I asked if she were pregnant, I would have discounted the answer. I think you can still discount the answer."

"Let's pull out the cecum," Dr. Busch tells Alison, who stands on her stool on the opposite side of the operating table.

"Let's see if the appendix is all right, which I think it is, but I hope it isn't."

Pulling out a rope of bowel, Alison brings the cecum forward into the wound. The appendix dangles like a finger from its intestinal pouch. The appendix is neither red nor swollen larger than usual.

"No, I don't think it is inflamed. I suspect a belly full of pus. Let's put her back in and we'll look at the pelvic organs, which I feel absolutely sure are inflamed."

A surgeon has walked into the O.R. and strides to the head of the O.R. table to peer at the girl's sleeping face. "What are you saying about this poor girl?" he smiles.

"Well, you know"—Dr. Busch stops and gestures with a free hand—"you can have"—he waves—"without V.D."

The surgeon's eyes above his mask crinkle into a smile. "You mean from the toilet seat?"

Alison has stuffed the string of bowel back into the open cavity.

Dr. Busch pokes at the abdominal organs, assessing problems by feel. "There's nothing much wrong with that ovary. Well, there's the tube. The tube is a little red. There's some fluid in there but not much. Let's culture that."

He hands a fluid-soaked sponge at the end of a sponge stick to the scrub nurse.

"There's pus!" he cries excitedly.

From her vantage point, Alison spots minute drops of pus on the right Fallopian tube. So much pain from such tiny pinpricks of yellow pus.

"We have a diagnosis. I want to culture that, too."

"Can you have that much pus and still not have it be venereal?" asks the onlooking surgeon tongue-in-cheek.

"I said, 'Listen, honey. If you can tell me that you have been making looove' "—Dr. Busch draws out the word—" 'In the last few days, then I can save you an operation.' She said, 'Uh, uh.' If she had told me yes, I wouldn't have operated. Obviously, the pelvic exam wasn't too impressive.''

"How does the other tube feel to you?" Dr. Busch asks Alison.

She feels deeply into the wound to touch the left tube. "It feels smaller than the other.''

"Then we'll take out her appendix and go home." In an exploratory procedure like this one, the appendix is routinely taken out to save the patient a possible operation later on in life.

"I've found from years of experience," he emphasizes to Alison, "that no matter how badly they feel, a young person isn't visibly too sick. There's peritoneal irritation all out of proportion to how they look. Now, why don't you tie the base with O chromic.''

Alison ties off the appendix near its base, cutting it off a little beyond the tie. She is careful to leave a sufficient whisker. She has seen the ligature slide off the slick appendiceal stump leaving the cecum gaping open and the abdomen filling with blood.

"Don't cut too close. Thatsagirl.''

"That's where I must have learned that expression," says Alison.

"I've used Polydek [a woven Dacron suture] for six months now to close the skin and I'm still not sure if I like it,'' says Dr. Busch.

"What did you use before?" Alison asks.

"I was a silk man." He pauses to qualify. "Except in cases of obvious infection.''

Jerry Kohler walks through the swinging O.R. doors to observe. Dr. Busch is pleased. "If we hadn't squeezed the tubes, we wouldn't have had a diagnosis,'' he says happily.

"Next time she'll be more careful when she—ahem" offers Kohler.

"What's that?" asks Busch as Kohler walks back out the doors.

Not lifting her eyes from the careful suturing, Alison interprets. "He was going to make a snotty remark about how next time she'll be more careful about choosing her partners.''

A 1970 article in the *New England Journal of Medicine* once compared the incidence of surgery in the United States to that in England and Wales, where the number of surgeons in proportion to population was about 50 percent less. The journal found a direct correlation between the numbers of surgeons and the total number of operations performed. The greater the number of surgeons, the greater the frequency of surgery. The article's physician-author was one of the first to document that the amount of surgery done is directly proportional to the number of surgeons available and to whether they receive a fee for each operation they do. About 80 percent of surgery in the United States is elective.

From her own experience, a fiftyish woman surgeon, presently responsible for overseeing the surgical training staff at a small urban hospital, would agree.

"There's been an increase of all kinds of surgery!" she cries. "And surgeons say this and they laugh. But I have the feeling that it's true. Why did you operate? Because it was like Mount Everest. Because the patient said yes. Then why did you tell the patient she needed it, or he needed it? Well, because it wouldn't hurt him.

"If doctors can strike and go eight weeks without operating, there must be an awful lot of surgery that could be either deferred or forgotten. In my special field, breast diseases, breasts are operated on—well, I forget the right word—unnecessarily. Incisional biopsies of tumors where the surgeon takes out a piece of the lump to see what it is. All these little things that women insist be done. The little repairs here and the tuck-up there.

"I mean, there are many women who are foolish. But they are aided and abetted by physicians who should know better. Perhaps in 'men's surgery' there is not that push because men are not sitting around all day going to doctors. And if you shave it down very carefully, women's surgery is more suspect than the surgery performed on men. Why? Because of its nature."

In a staccato she says, "It's-not-really-necessary. I mean, it might be necessary for the patient, but I'm not sure that that's right either.

"I'm sure that if we didn't train another surgeon for twenty years, we'd still have plenty; we just need people working in hospitals while they're getting their training. At this hospital I tease and suggest that they take more women interns. After all, people say that women doctors are not going to work.

"Administratively, I am responsible for the patients, and occasionally I'll go in and talk to them, you know, and see what brought them here into the hospital. Most of it is not liberated thinking. I mean, I'm sure that it's *important,* but you know that they did not decide for themselves. Most of the lady patients here do what their husbands tell them to do. They're traditional. They may *work,* but they're still traditional. They don't question. You have to tell them, 'Look, you don't have to do what your husband says.'

" 'Don't tell her she has cancer.' I've met that many times. And I say I'll never tell anybody anything except I'll never lie. And if she comes out and asks me 'Do I have cancer?' I will have to say something. I may not use the term. Usually you say, 'Well, what is cancer?' And by the time they get finished defining it, you find a little phrase in there that you can use. My favorite reminder is the name of New York City's Memorial Hospital which says the hospital is for 'Cancer and Allied Diseases.' Everybody knows that they're in there for the allied diseases.

"I would insist upon being told if I had cancer. I would insist upon it and I would strangle anybody who lied to me. Not the day of surgery, because nobody remembers what happens the day of surgery. And anybody who lies to me is in trouble, even just to save me. Because I can handle anything if you share it with me, but I can't share something I don't know."

Alison, on the other hand, feels that too many lay people associate elective surgery with unnecessary surgery. "Just because an operation can wait one or two months," she explains, "doesn't mean it shouldn't be done three months from now. I remember once reading that some 5,000 deaths a year are ascribed to hernias which were never repaired. In England, there are long waits for hospital beds."

In Room 822, Alison Merrill stops to talk to a woman patient of Dr. Mills.

"I took a sleeping pill," Clare Rittenberg gushes to Alison when she walks up to her bedside, "and I went out." She pretends to collapse her head on the pillow. "And then I got up and went to the bathroom and I was so groggy I didn't remember you wanted a urine specimen first thing in the morning."

Mrs. Rittenberg is complaining of vague sharp pain in the lower abdomen and is due to be explored surgically later today. Yesterday she mentioned to Alison in passing that she thought she might be pregnant. Alison wanted her first, concentrated morning urine to ascertain whether or not she is indeed pregnant.

The woman has left a second specimen in the bathroom which will later prove negative.

"She's a strange lady," says Alison after leaving Mrs. Rittenberg's room. "She's only twenty-eight and this is her second gynecological surgery. I thought, Ohmigod! I don't want to do exploratory surgery on a lady who is pregnant. You should be very careful when you don't know exactly what you are going in for." Mrs. Rittenberg's physicians have not yet pinpointed the cause of her pain. They hope to discover her problem under the knife.

When Alison reports that Mrs. Rittenberg mentioned she might be pregnant, Dr. Mills shakes his head and discounts that particular possibility. She's had so much hormonal therapy, she couldn't possibly be pregnant, he tells Alison.

Alison's next task takes her to O.R. 4, where she will first-assist Dr. Mills in inserting prosthetic implants under folds of breast tissue. Two soft, circular, clear plastic envelopes filled with waterlike silicone will be tucked under the overlying breast flap, and the new scars will be hidden in the inframammary fold. The fifty-two-year-old woman patient has undergone a bilateral mastectomy six months earlier.

"This is a procedure," explains Alison, "which is strictly for benign breast disease for women who carry a reasonable amount of pride about themselves. The implants make it more acceptable to women to lose their breast. There are sometimes so many lumps, the best thing is to cut off the breast. From month to month the surgeon can't be sure there won't be carcinoma."

The original surgery left behind a scar in the inframammary fold and the overlying skin of the breasts, which are strangely flat.

Alison holds up the edges of the breast fold with clamps while Dr. Mills alternately cuts a little above the inframammary fold and sponges the area dry.

"The skin was a little firm from the scar," Alison said later. "And more resistive to cut into."

The scrub nurse hands Dr. Mills one prosthesis, which looks less like a breast than a round, transparent jellyfish.

Taking it with his gloved hand, Dr. Mills had trouble stuffing the prosthesis into the small incision in order to puff up the breast.

He frowns and looks at the prosthetic effect from all directions. "We could use a bigger size on her," he concludes. "I'm not too impressed, are you?" he asks his female entourage, which includes Alison, a scrub nurse, and a circulating nurse.

"Have you got 200 cc.? If you've got 200 cc.s, she'll look better than she ever did. How long will it take you to get bigger ones?"

The circulating nurse leaves and slowly reenters bearing a styrofoam box containing larger prostheses. "I've got 200s here."

"Of course, when you lie down it all flattens out," reflects Dr. Mills, looking at his patient's chest. "Let's see the bigger ones. They might look better."

The nurse offers to autoclave the bigger prostheses, putting them in special apparatus with sterilizing pressurized steam. Dr. Mills decides not to wait but to go ahead with the smaller set, which are already sterile and ready to be implanted.

Sewing the implant into place, Alison feels like ramming the needle through the slightly rigid scar tissue but is afraid she might poke a hole in the prosthesis and the implant might leak like a sieve.

"She had great big cysts in her breasts," says Dr. Mills of his patient. "Fibrocystic disease. When I first told her that she should have her breasts removed she protested. 'Oh, no! I can't do that.' Then I talked about a prosthesis and she said she might consider *that.* She was extremely neurotic about losing her breasts."

The circulating nurse is walking around the O.R. table toward a kickbucket with some discarded bloody sponges clamped onto the end of a sponge stick.

"It's the exact same thing for a testicle," she shoots back quickly. "They make the same kind of implants for a male testicle if it is important to a man to keep his contours in the locker room or the bedroom."

Dr. Mills listens gracefully.

Later, Alison and Eva Belman walk into O.R. 6 to watch the end of a gallbladder removal. To protect the sterile field, a bouffant cap, like the classic nurses' cap, hides away the hair of the patient on the table. The outlines of the form under the drapes are soft and chubby and somewhat feminine. Jerry Kohler, who has been a member of the surgical team, is finishing removing the sheet-sized drapes from the patient.

Her hands on her hips, Alison looks hard at the body of the obviously male patient as it is uncovered. "Oh!" she says, surprised. "I thought it was a woman!"

"They're all the same under the sheets," comments Eva.

Kohler looks up quickly. "No, they're not." He grins suggestively.

Alison glances over at Eva, who looks embarrassed and crestfallen. She should have known better than to make a comment with a sexual double meaning. Eva's remark just slipped out unintentionally.

Later in the O.R. Clare Rittenberg is stretched out on the table. An obstetrician-gynecologist is positioned on one side of the table and Dr. Mills on the other. For a surgical procedure called an exploratory laparotomy, they have made a midline incision in a straight line from the umbilicus to explore her abdomen from a variety of angles. Alison stands on the sidelines, watching briefly. She has just dropped by.

"What did you find?" Dr. Mills asks of Dr. Youngdell, the obstetrician-gynecologist and his surgical colleague. Mrs. Rittenberg was originally a patient of Dr. Youngdell, who called in Dr. Mills.

"Some pelvic adhesions. Nothing more yet." Dr. Youngdell is feeling deeply into the incision. "She also has a band over her ovaries which is sort of strange." Adhesions from previous surgery have formed a constricting band.

Dr. Mills feels too. "The kidneys are fine. What do you want to do about that ovary?"

The gray-haired gynecologist thinks for a moment. "I wonder if I should open it."

"That would be meddlesome."

A nurse steps quickly into the O.R. "Dr. Youngdell. Her pains are less than two minutes apart." Another of Dr. Youngdell's patients is about to deliver in a different part of the hospital.

Dr. Mills stamps his foot. "Oh, damn it."

"She wants to know if she can have an epidural," reports the nurse.

"Yeah. Let her have an epidural." Dr. Youngdell bends over the surgical field and peers into the wound, never lifting his head. "This is a remarkable lady. She has two ovaries on the right and none on the left."

"If you're through diddling with that, let's go look at the appendectomy and we can come back."

In singsong, Dr. Mills asks the scrub nurse, "May I have some tapes please?"

Both Dr. Mills and Dr. Youngdell proceed to tie and cut off the appendix from the small intestine.

"Forgive them," says Dr. Mills, "for they know not what they do."

Alison is now standing close to the table in her usual stance of repose with her hands on her hips. She is not scrubbed.

"Do you want to go upstairs and help this other woman have a baby?" Dr. Mills asks of his colleague.

Dr. Youngdell shrugs. "Yeah, that would be nice." He strips off his gloves and drops them into a kickbucket, then throws his gown into a hamper parked next to the tiled O.R. wall.

In addition to removing Mrs. Rittenberg's appendix, the surgical team has lysed, or cut, the tight fibrous scar circling one ovary.

"What are we going to tell her husband?" asks Dr. Youngdell of Dr. Mills with an embarrassed grunt.

"We'll straightforwardly tell him what we found and what we didn't find."

# 31
# Tomorrow I Will Be Very Smart

9:00 A.M. Sunday.

It's the last day of her Lakeside rotation, and Alison has been on call all weekend. "I really can't imagine a life as a physician's wife," she sighs. "It must be hard to be married to someone who is never home, who is often too tired to talk to his spouse. I don't know how the wives tolerate it. I would hate it on the other side of the fence."

For their first wedding anniversary in June, Mike turned the tables on Alison quite unintentionally. Alison carefully coordinated plans with the other residents to ensure she would not be on call that night. She made a tangle of long, involved phone calls to protect the privacy of that evening. She came home early that day. She imagined a quiet, cozy dinner for two at home. Candlelight and more. But she was surprised to find that Mike had made other plans. Arriving home, he announced that he was playing in a Westinghouse League softball tournament that evening. Before reaching their apartment he had intended to buy flowers. However, he was caught by the swirl of commuter traffic and arrived later than he had anticipated. He had to decide which he had time for, buying flowers or playing softball. To Alison's acute annoyance, he chose softball.

The playing field was an hour away. The other men were with wives and girlfriends she didn't know. So she sat up in the bleachers, essentially alone.

It wasn't too difficult for Mike to discern that Alison was sulking.

She didn't talk, she didn't smile, she glared. At one time she said she was going to wait in the car. Alison's mother-in-law claims that it was six months before Alison would talk to Mike again.

But Mike honestly could not imagine what had gone awry. "Why are you so upset, Alison?" he asked gently. "At least we are together for our anniversary. At least we're doing something together for once."

To make matters worse, Mike's team lost.

Mike never got around to buying her flowers for that anniversary. "I guess I blew it," he said later.

After flipping through patients' charts at the nurses' station on 5 South, Alison talks briefly about Frank Nesbitt, another resident in her year of training, whom she has found interesting and easy to talk to. Perhaps because Alison was a woman and he was having marital problems, he had at one time confided in her.

Up until late in the year, Frank Nesbitt had been a compulsive surgical resident. An otherwise jovial fellow, he might suddenly bolt upright at 3:00 A.M. during an on-call night, remembering he had neglected to tell the nurses on the floor to prep a certain patient for surgery the next morning. Most residents would have said the hell with it and gone back to sleep, thinking, If it doesn't get done now, I can always take care of it when I get up in the morning. A resident might go to bed at four o'clock and remember, Jeez, I forgot to look at Mrs. Parks's X-rays. But then he'd consider that the I.C.U. or the floor might call in the next hour or two and if he had to get up, he would do it then. Frank really loved his surgical residency and was always *there.* Even on his nights off he was home very late, because he would stay at the hospital and get everything done before he left, or try to. But his wife didn't share his enthusiasm for his work. She figured that if he didn't care enough to come home early on the nights he was *off,* never mind not being home at all every third night, she didn't have to stick around. So she just left and never came back. Later she filed for a divorce.

"It was an enormous shock to him," says Alison. "With time, he decided that he would have to change if he was going to have any kind of life outside the hospital. Now he is living with one of the nurses. When he finishes his training, he wants to be a nine-to-five surgeon. He wants to get up and operate, repair a couple of hernias, maybe a gallbladder, make rounds, see some people in his office, and go home and forget about surgery. He does not want multiple trauma dropping on his doorstep. He does not want people with acute emergencies disrupting his carefully structured practice.

"You can set up your practice one way or the other, like Dr. Busch does. A very, very nice person and a good technical surgeon, Dr. Busch does not like coming in in the middle of the night and he lets that be *known.* At night, his referring physicians call somebody else. Whereas Dr. Ness is thrilled by the midnight emergencies, the drama, the trauma, the gore and excitement. Look at the countless number of nights that Dr. Ness is up doing cases. You can look at that and say to yourself, Do I want to be a resident for the rest of my life? Only it's worse than being a resident, because it turns out that instead of every third night, you're on call *every* night. Many of the residents look forward to spending a little more time with their families after they finish their rigorous training."

Two weeks ago, a resident's wife delivered a baby by Caesarian section. Jon Salz left only for the morning his wife delivered, made rounds in the afternoon, and went back to visit her that night. A few days after she came home, his wife developed a temperature of 104°. As a special favor, Jon Salz asked Alison if she could take his night calls while he went home to nurse his sick wife and attend the new baby. Alison readily agreed. Jon Salz needed all the help he could get.

Then the next week, Chris Fritsch's wife, who has two children, fell ill. In order to help him, Alison switched on-call nights with Chris, so that he could drive home to care for his family.

At Journal Club, where each resident presents the gist of a journal article he has read to the other residents, the hospital's chief of surgery was baffled by the poor attendance. Taking a look around a relatively empty room, Dr. Webster asked, "I know Berger is on vacation, but where is Fritsch?" Someone spoke up and said his wife had become sick and he was forced to go home.

The chief of surgery exploded. He was furious that Chris Fritsch was the second resident in a week to excuse himself from his hospital duties to tend a sick wife. Residents were not supposed to be married. Certainly they were not to be allowed to go *home* because their wives were sick.

"You're basically expected to call up neighbors and ask them to come take care of your sick spouse,'' Alison translated later. It is the old-fashioned point of view from the time when entering medical school was regarded as joining a temporary celibate priesthood. Sir William Osler once suggested to medical students in a solemn medical journal ''to put your affections in cold storage for a few years.''

At the close of Journal Club, after Dr. Webster had left the conference room, Alison asked her fellow residents what day next week she could plan to have *her husband* sick, since two of them had already rearranged their schedules to care for their wives. Already rattled, the other residents cast her vile looks, remarking that her suggestion was completely humorless.

Alison is now being paged to dial the hospital operator. ''Three thousand and one medical problems,'' she grumbles after taking the call, ''and I have to put in an I.V. This is something Medicine could handle, but they've decided the surgical resident should do it. It's supposed to be a goddamn surgical procedure.''

She has just been asked to insert an intravenous line into the subclavian vein of a male patient who is suffering from congestive heart failure. The subclavian vein empties into the superior vena cava, which in turn joins the right atrium. Since there are no valves to interrupt blood flow in these vessels, the blood-pressure reading through the subclavian I.V. hookup will be consistent with right atrial pressure. In addition, the subclavian I.V. offers a medication route close to the heart, circumventing an impaired circulation as effectively as possible. She turns in the direction of 3 North.

Walking briskly, she can hear the patient's screams loudly echoing into the hall before she even reaches his room.

An older, square-faced man lies on his back, tossing his head violently from side to side on the bed. ''Please, my God, my God. Let me wet just one time.'' He closes his eyes, moans and grimaces with pain. Supplementary oxygen is being pumped into a green tube through his nose.

In congestive heart failure the heart pump has stopped functioning properly and the blood is no longer circulated efficiently. With a sluggish circulation, the blood tends to sit in the lungs' capillaries, impairing the total exchange of oxygen and carbon dioxide.

''He keeps pulling out his tubes,'' a nurse complains to Alison.

Asking the nurse for gloves, Alison carefully sprays the area of the neck with Betadine and drapes the patient's head and neck with sterile blue paper towels.

The man's bladder is catheterized with a thick tube running from his penis, yet he screams, "Jesus Christ, have mercy on my soul. I've got to go to the bathroom so bad."

"Honey, you can go as soon as we're done," Alison replies, trying to soothe him long enough so she can get her work finished. She will try to figure out his predicament after she inserts the I.V.

The man's face has completely disappeared from view.

"Now, you're going to feel a little stick here and a little burning. We've put on a topical anesthetic to deaden the pain."

Alison begins to gently thread the catheter down through the neck's internal jugular vein, down eight or ten inches where the jugular branches into the subclavian vein below the clavicle. She is careful to proceed cautiously to avoid punching a hole in the left lung as the subclavian I.V. catheter passes over its tip.

"Ow. Ow. Ow." Dark blood gushes out of the syringe and spurts over Alison's gloves and the towels.

"Oh, I've got to go to the bathroom."

Finishing the last detail of the job she was requested to do, Alison sews the intravenous tubing firmly into place.

From another phone, the patient's private doctor is asking for a routine chest X-ray to check the placement of the subclavian line.

Beads of perspiration cover the patient's face.

Puzzled, Alison fingers the urinary line. She wonders if the Foley catheter is blocked so that the patient is unable to eliminate, but then she notices urine coming through the line. The more likely option is that the patient is feeling pressure from the Foley catheter's balloon placed in his bladder, giving him the impression his bladder is full. Eventually that sensation of fullness will disappear.

"You have a tube in you," she informs the man. "Try to calm yourself."

As she leaves the room, she looks idly into the adjacent glassed-in waiting room, where she notices a young boy and an older woman, slumped into their armchairs. Probably the man's family.

"The man already has only marginal cardiac performance," says Alison, now walking at a normal pace down the hall. "He'll kill himself if he doesn't relax."

She realizes that she has inadvertently taken a patient's card from the I.C.U. "They're going to be after me any moment."

She ducks down the stairs in the direction of the surgical I.C.U. Blood from the I.V. has splattered both her scrubs and her white coat.

In the I.C.U. she returns the card to an unworried nurse seated at the nurses' station and spots Thayer Davey and John Peltzer. "Do you want to work up the admissions for tomorrow?" she asks them. Each admission will take a minimum of forty-five minutes. "Dr. Laramy has a hernia case. Mills has a gastrostomy who has been here twenty thousand times. There's a thyroid for Mills and a sphinctero-plasty that should be seen. There are nine admissions, and I'll never be able to see all of them."

"Tell us which ones you want to do," says John.

They discuss the new patients at further length, and John and Thayer make out their list.

The dits and dots of the EKG monitors blip by at the nurses' station but no one seems to have time to watch.

In the I.C.U. Alison checks on Ann Stuart, a thirty-two-year-old patient with liver cancer who has recently undergone a surgical procedure. The woman's mother stands silently, sadly at her bedside spooning mouthfuls of food into her mouth. Eyes closed, Ann Stuart seems too weary to move her head. Her mouth mechanically opens and closes, and her skin is the color of a grocery bag.

"Do you feel weak or dizzy?" Alison asks her softly.

"Very . . . very . . . weak." Ann Stuart is speaking very, very softly.

"Have you felt this way before?"

"No . . . not before . . . I can't breathe." Ann Stuart's whisper is barely audible.

"She's had nausea and vomiting today," her mother elaborates.

"I'm . . . so . . . short . . . of breath." Ann Stuart looks as if she were simply waiting for doom.

Alison listens to her lungs with her stethoscope. "Sounds good." Next she examines Ann Stuart's charts.

"Do we have any lytes on her recently?" Alison is asking the nurse for a recent lab check on the woman's electrolyte balance.

"No. She didn't have any lab work ordered for today. It's ordered for tomorrow."

"She might be hypovolemic." The woman's fluids circulating through her body may have dropped drastically.

Alison walks out of Ann Stuart's room to call her surgeon, Dr. Ness, from a phone at the I.C.U. nurses' station. "I don't know,"

Alison puzzles out loud after she asks a nurse for Dr. Ness's telephone number. "I think she's just suffering from acute 'termies.'" Alison believes Ann Stuart is suffering from a multitude of problems stemming from a terminal illness.

At the I.C.U. nurses' station, Alison dials Dr. Ness's number. "Dr. Ness, how are you doing? . . . Ann Stuart, O.K.?" Alison laughs at something Dr. Ness says, then describes a sudden drop of pressure in his patient.

"She was supposed to get a crit [a hematocrit to measure the red blood cell mass, a test for anemia] this morning, which never got drawn. I thought I'd let you know. Oh, I put a subclavian in. The chest X-ray shows the entire left side is practically all her heart. [Mrs. Stuart's heart is enlarged.] It doesn't look like there is a pneumothorax from a subclavian [an accidental introduction of air in the thorax from a lung puncture caused by trauma from the subclavian catheter], so what can I say?"

Off the phone, she instructs a young I.C.U. nurse. "Give her protein and fluids so her pressure will go up slightly."

"Dr. Merrill, this is your last day, isn't it? Do you know who comes on next?"

Alison is not sure.

"Tomorrow I change to University Hospital," Alison remarks. "I don't know what floor I'm supposed to report to, whether I'm supposed to go to the surgical floor or the E.R. I'll go there tomorrow and page the chief resident, whose name I heard through the grapevine, and say, 'Hey, what's happening, kid?'"

Leafing through yet another buttercup yellow chart, she mutters, "Gastrectomy for a duodenal ulcer. Obesity, upper G.I. bleed, hypertension. A great case. I'm glad I'm not going to be here tomorrow."

Alison goes to see a patient she describes as a "nice, pleasant old lady."

"Mrs. Sundquist, I'm Dr. Laramy's resident. Just want to know if you have any questions before tomorrow."

The gray-haired lady shakes her head, "No."

"You have an excellent surgeon."

"That's always good news."

"You're going to get a unit of blood."

"Now?"

"In two minutes."

The cheery, relaxed lady seems to be in no pain.

A nurse comes up with a packaged unit of blood.

Leaving the patient's room, Alison explains that she has been bleeding internally, as evidenced by her pitch-black stools. "Basically people tolerate anesthesia better if they're less anemic," says Alison, explaining why the woman is to receive a transfusion.

"Tomorrow I'm going to be very smart," she laughs, writing her notes on the patient's chart. Tomorrow, she begins a new year and a new title: junior resident. The new junior assistant residents will now be assisting her.

Alison feels there has been a very subtle improvement in her self-confidence and ability to care for very sick patients. It is not something she noticed from one day to the next. There was no one momentous milestone against which to measure her progress.

At the start of the first residency year, if someone had arrived at the E.R. with an extensive, bleeding laceration, she might have grumbled to herself; "Ohmigod! What am I going to do? I know it started in one piece, but how am I going to get it all back together?" She now knows how to clean the injured area thoroughly, to order a tetanus shot for the patient, to clamp the big blood vessels, to compress the smaller ones with stitches; exactly how to close the muscle, the subcutaneous tissue, and finally the skin, and what suture to use. The flesh begins to fall back into place as she skillfully brings each layer together.

Certainly she had learned erudite facts in medical school, but most important was a change in her own attitude during this first year of residency: a recognition that she had mastered some of the clinical skills necessary for proper care of her patients. At some point during this year she no longer felt the need to call somebody over to help.

In a few days she would read the yearlong progression in herself by comparison with the unsure faces of the new interns, whose tortured expressions seemed to be saying, "Ohmigod! What am I supposed to do next?"

# Epilogue

*"You can be a wonderful doctor and not care about power, but the moment you go into a hospital and want to be chief surgical resident, you might as well, in power terms, be working for a large corporation."*
—Michael Korda, author of *Power! How to Get It, How to Use It*

In the fall of her second year in training in general surgery, Alison Merrill received a disturbing summons. Would she please come see Dr. DeKay, the executive director of the Department of Surgery, at her earliest convenience about a matter which could not be discussed over the phone? Could she wait a week or so, she asked? No, Dr. DeKay's secretary insisted, sometime in the next few days would be more appropriate. At the time, she felt clearly rattled. There were very few things Dr. DeKay would want to talk to her about in intimate privacy, and very few matters which could not be discussed over the phone.

The pyramid system in the general surgery residency program had turned the years of training into a domino system. Even with twelve well-qualified residents in the initial year, there was room at the top for only four chief residents in the final fifth year. And only after a year as chief resident could a resident be eligible to take the American Board of Surgery's stiff exams for certification.

In addition to the ever-present threat of a pyramiding system, University Hospital's particular program had been abbreviated after Alison's arrival from a six- to a five-year program, with the squeeze

person. A woman in surgery has to be, a woman in a man's world.

"I haven't heard of any specific instance of bad judgment, and the training program is so structured that you are brought along slowly to avoid the chance of very serious error. I think that decisions are quickly made in the first few months of internship. My feeling is that when Alison first started, she was a little insecure. There's the initial shock of an intern facing people for the first time who die on you. In my own case, it took a considerable amount of time before I felt comfortable when confronted with dying patients. By the time she reached City Hospital, she was ahead of where you would expect her to be. But first impressions count. The people at the top don't have time to know you personally. They hear little things which then color their opinions.

"There are so many women in medicine now—there's been such a change in the last three or four years—that they just blend in the wards. I don't think that Alison's being a woman was an element at all."

Carol Carse shrugs cynically. "Alison was under a lot of pressure. I remember that when I arrived at City Hospital and Dave Fayard saw that both Alison and I were assigned to him, he joked that he had gotten the females this time. If people doubt your competence, then they just keep waiting around for you to mess up.

"I don't think that the student ratings, for one, mean a thing. You see people who work very hard who don't get good reports, and people who work very little who get beautiful, enthusiastic reports. There are politics involved. It all depends on who you know, how you impress the residents, and if they like you.

"Personally, I've developed the attitude that I don't care. At City Hospital, I covered for Kirstin so many times. I was there much more than that child, sometimes until 10:00 at night, covering for her while she was running around with a pediatrician at University Hospital. Then my student report read something like 'She only showed interest in the assigned patients and did average work,' while Kirstin got a high pass for that rotation and I got a pass. The residents at City Hospital liked her.

"I don't care"—Carol is choking—"because at City Hospital I was there for those patients.

"In order to apply for a residency," Carol continues, "I had to ask one of the deans for a recommendation. He wrote something to the effect that this student will become a fair physician if she becomes more academically inclined; that my situation could be understood from a minority point of view; that it had been such a struggle for all of us to get through. I called his secretary to tell her that I felt that dean's letter was an exaggeration and that I thought his letter would be a disadvantage. I got a letter back saying that he couldn't change what he had said; that any changes would work to my disadvantage; that in any case he couldn't change the letter because everything he said was true.''

"Alison started on the *worst* rotation," Craig Armstrong offers, mentioning Dr. Witter's cardiovascular service, which handles a very high number of patients per number of residents.

"In the beginning, it took Alison a little longer than the rest of us, who had gone to University Hospital's medical school, to get an I.V. started. She knew her pathology, she had very good academic training. But as far as her clinical training—inserting I.V.'s and drawing blood—she was just a little bit behind.

"All the residents have advisers. I asked mine how a resident was supposed to be able to judge his performance. 'We'll let you know.' No one I've talked to has been able to tell me.

"I know there was a move to make several cuts and to bring in people from the outside. There was a feeling that the surgical program here was becoming too ingrown with too many residents who had graduated from University Medical School. The big schools—Hopkins, Yale, Harvard—have a built-in surgical pyramid. When these residents get dropped, they still look very good. University Hospital felt it was time we started exposing ourselves to different methods.

"Alison never shirked her duties and she was totally competent. Some residents, you know, can pawn off their responsibilities. We were all kind of surprised when we heard about it, but you always live with that shadow of possible rejection over you.''

One surgical resident, whose discontent is so deep he has since left surgery altogether, feels that surgical training programs are totalitarian and feudal. "The program is full of megalomaniacs. These men talk down to you. Your ego is knocked down fifteen steps.

"There was one resident who was told he had to repeat his third year because of a supposed error in judgment. This sort of thing happens all the time. But there are all sorts of eyes watching to capitalize on any mistakes they can.

"What happens if you should complain to your advisers? They are university professors who are clubbish and oligarchical, and who want to keep their positions of affluence and power. It's like preserving the brotherhood of the Black Hand.

"Frankly," he says. "it's a little like the army, with the surgical resident as an enlisted man. You take orders because your superiors hold a position of power over you. You put yourself in jeopardy if you're at all independent. The future is ambiguous unless you're well behaved, well liked, and submissive. In time, you learn not to speak up, to hold in your grudges, and hold tight until your board exams."

No official decision was ever made as to whether or not Alison would be able to become a chief resident at University Hospital. But after her talk with Dr. DeKay, she decided that rather than stay an additional year she would leave as soon as her present year was finished. She found another appointment in a surgical training program at a smaller community hospital without a pyramid system which promised her a surgical chiefship at the top. The second hospital was in the same geographic area as the University Medical Center, so that Mike was not forced to change jobs, which he was very reluctant to do since he had seniority at Westinghouse. When the new hospital asked her during an initial interview if she felt her predicament had arisen from the fact that she was a woman, Alison played down the possibility. "They may have been asking the question to see if they were getting a troublemaker," she explained later.

"I hope that University Hospital originally noticed me more as a woman," she laughs. "I could very easily say that, you know, people don't like me because I'm a woman in surgery. But my basic reaction when I hear a critique of my performance is to tell myself that I will have to get on my toes and do better the next time. But I get very upset in that respect because I don't ever really know if my being a woman is a factor in the way I am being evaluated. Whether they look more carefully for things that I might do wrong, I'll never know. But I never make the assumption that people are necessarily treating me unfairly because I'm a woman.

"I like it better here in this program. The surgical attendings talk to you like someone who has actually graduated from medical school. I think that at University Hospital there was a definite tendency toward one-upmanship. They wanted you to finish your training and get out. The surgical attendings, I felt, didn't want you settling down in the area and competing with them. I've done more surgical cases here in one month than in three months at University Hospital.

"University Hospital was a cliquey group. A lot of residents had gone to medical school there and stayed on for a residency. They all knew each other. I never felt like one of them. The other two women in the surgical program have gone into surgical subspecialties and dropped out of the competition for chief resident. Of the original group, I am the only woman to have continued in general surgery.

"Mike and I fit in better down here. I feel when people invite us to dinner or to a party, it's because they enjoy our company, not because they feel obligated to ask us. It's even reflected in the fact that Mike will periodically come by the hospital here to see me, something he never did before. The people here are much more friendly, and if I get called away Mike will even stop and pass the time chatting with the other residents. It wasn't that the people at University Hospital were truly snobbish. It was more a reserved friendliness. Mike never liked to go to large social occasions and big affairs where the people were all my friends and he didn't know anybody there. Basically, Mike is very shy. But people here make an effort to talk to him.

"It was a good thing to make this change. I think that first year I spent a lot of evenings talking with Mike. I might have spent too much time relaxing with him. Now I keep up with my surgical journals assiduously and read about my cases *well* in advance of surgery. I think I would still have made a good surgeon without that professional jolt, but I think I am a better physician for it now."